SECOND CROP

SECOND CROP

Paul Heiney

H. F. & G. WITHERBY

First published in Great Britain 1993
by H. F. & G. Witherby
A Cassell imprint
Villiers House, 41/47 Strand, London WC2N 5JE

© Paul Heiney 1993
Illustrations © Joe Wright 1993

A catalogue record for this book is
available from the British Library

ISBN 0 85493 235 6

Photoset in Great Britain by
Rowland Phototypesetting Ltd, Bury St Edmunds, Suffolk
and printed by St Edmundsbury Press Ltd,
Bury St Edmunds, Suffolk

To Nicholas and Rose

Contents

Acknowledgements 9

Introduction 11

1 Good Ideas and Good Intentions 13

2 New Loves (And an Old Friend Goes) 37

3 Keeping Crops on the Straight and Narrow 59

4 Well, It's a Point of View 73

5 Animals! The Dramatic Truth 97

6 Rats Fight Back Too 119

7 Man Versus Machine (And a Young Horse to Add to the Confusion) 131

8 Endless Torment 147

9 Hallelujah! The Year is Done 169

Acknowledgements

I would like to thank *The Times* in which these columns were first published. After three years I am still flattered that they should consider them to be worthy of publication and I thank Sue Peart and Jane Owen who have proved patient and understanding editors. I must also thank Joe the illustrator who gives each column his individual and unfailingly witty embellishment. He makes me laugh out loud every week.

At home, my wife and family have borne my farming career with great fortitude and patience, often beyond the call of duty.

For some reason I cannot imagine, my team of helpers and mentors has not run out on me yet either. We still have regular visits from Derek Filby the horseman, Dilly Sharp the retired farm-hand, Richard and Margaret White and their son Robert, Sebastian Hall, John Cousins the thatcher, and Richard Jones. I have also turned to my old friends Roger and Cheryl Clark when needing good advice on working horses and traditional farming practices and our vets Philip Ryder-Davies and Dick Smith have answered our calls for help with speed and to beneficial effect.

Introduction

I am now into my third year as a farmer. But I would not wish you to believe for one minute that it is getting any easier. As regular readers of my Saturday *Times* column (and those who bought the first collection, *Farming Times*) will know, I set out full of optimism to re-create on our small farm in Suffolk an image of what I considered to be the golden age of agriculture.

I place great emphasis on the word *agriculture* for my motives have occasionally been misunderstood. I have no wish to return to the poverty, exploitation and deprivation of the first fifty years of this century. It was not my intention to send my children to school with rickets just to satisfy some nostalgic fantasy. No: farmers and farmhands a hundred years ago may have had hard lives, but I'm damned if they didn't know how to farm. It is often said by farmers round here who wish to put down one of their fellows: 'He's not half the farmer his father was. And his father wasn't half the farmer *his* father was!' Well, I wanted to be Granddad, who had no access to the modern battery of chemicals to feed on to the land and into his livestock. I wanted to be a farmer who walked the land and by doing so learned every one of its ways, so that by the time I had served my apprenticeship, I would be the conductor, directing a symphony of natural processes which would come together as a farm. What's more, I was not going to use tractors. I would use cart-horses, Suffolk Punches in their native county.

The dream was fine, the awakening has often been a rude one. But we have tried to bear it all with good humour and when that has failed we have gone and kicked the barn door (the cat having learned to hide). Most of the characters you might have met in my first collection of columns have not deserted us, although I have no doubt they were tempted at times. Our cart-horses, Star, Prince and Blue, still stand in the stable. Alice, the Large Black sow, sits regally in her sty. She wishes you to know that she deplores the publication of this book and is heartily sick of her private life being put on public gaze. Sorry, Alice; but like farming, the show must go on.

1
Good Ideas
and
Good Intentions

B AD NEWS. I am moving out. Not immediately, but certainly by this time next year I shall be living elsewhere – assuming I can find a sufficiently inventive estate agent who can come up with the accommodation that I am looking for. My requirements are quite strict.

I have in mind something basic, but certainly with character. I am not too worried about spaciousness; just enough room to stretch out will do nicely. But heating is going to be very important, and so is waterproofing. I am not too worried about how much land it has, for I have sufficient of that already. I also ought to mention that it has to be on wheels, and preferably made of wood.

The move arises because I can no longer pretend I am an adequate shepherd if I conduct my lambing from beneath the comfort of a multi-tog duvet. The wicked mistress of the electric blanket too easily seduces me away from the essential marriage between a shepherd and his flock at lambing time. So next year I am going to do my duty properly, and as it does not seem reasonable to have the sheep move into the house, I am going to live with them.

Shepherds always used to live with their flocks at lambing time, and many still camp out in caravans. But I have it in mind to find myself a traditional shepherd's hut of the kind which moved from field to field, and in which the flockmaster spent long months of the year. They were cosy little vans: a cross between a railway waggon and a ship's cabin, with a cheery little billy-stove round which to warm sickly lambs. Shepherds, I read, had other ways of warming themselves: sickly lambs were thought to thrive on a quick sip of whisky administered by the shepherd swilling it first round his own mouth and then spitting it into the lamb's. Several doses per night probably did little for the poor creature but no doubt kept the shepherd cheerful at what can be a depressing time.

For lambing is depressing. It is one of the crescendos of the farming year, played out against a background of new-born bleats and milky, mothering ewes. But only in retrospect do I find joy at lambing time. As I look at our pen of healthy bouncing lambs, cavorting in and out of the hay and fighting their early battles at the trough; when I see the energy with which those stubby little tails shake when their owners have successfully latched on to mother's teat; when I walk around in the evening and the round-bellied little creatures are asleep while the ewes keep watch, I find it easy to forget the anguish that has got us this far.

But I never do entirely forget it. It is not possible to be unmoved by the sight of a ewe trying with all her might to lick life into her stillborn lamb. It is a pitiful business to have to drag dead lambs from the wombs of otherwise healthy ewes. But the worst thing of all is the suspicion that you, as shepherd, may in any way be responsible for a lamb losing its life.

So far I have been dutiful and made visits to the pens last thing at night, once in the early hours and again at breakfast, but some nights ago, after a hard week of late bed-times and early risings I took a night off, had a few drinks, and slept long and hard. It was too long. By the time I was at the lambing pen, a couple of hours later than usual, there were four dead lambs: two sets of twins. They were sealed in the sac in which they were born and had they been able to take those first vital gasps of air, they might have lived. But I was not there to help them, not around to stick a quick finger in their mouths, feel the lamb's first sucking reflex as it tried to squeeze milk from the finger. I was not there to oversee those first brave stumbling steps as the bleary lamb makes its way to the teat. I have now watched calves, lambs and piglets make those faltering steps and it is without doubt the bravest little journey in the world.

But all I had were four corpses and a couple of bewildered mothers, confused by their loyalties, which seemed divided between their dead lambs and the anticipation of food. Within the hour, healthy thriving twins were born, then triplets, and the heart rose again – until a late-night check revealed one of the twins to have died and then the nagging thoughts began: could I have done more?

Next year it will be different. If I can find a shepherd's hut I shall move in with them. I know it is not smart these days for farmers to confess any affection for their flocks, and hard-headed commercial farmers will already have written lambing losses into the balance sheet, but I am fond of the old ewes. And for the few short weeks of the year when they need me, I must be there. Full time.

I T IS NOT USUAL for farmers to discuss their emotions. In fact, the whole agonising business of rearing animals and growing crops requires the farmer to dull his personal sensitivities to the point of extinction. Mine are virtually gone. I can remember a time when every coughing lamb or limping piglet was a matter of deep and lasting grief, but not any longer. They still get swift attention but it is more in a workmanlike frame of mind than a spiritual one.

However, there is still one area of my life where I am considering closer identification with my animals. It is in the matter of personal magnetism. You see, I was not born to be a ladykiller. Some men, blessed with a mysterious animal magnetism, have only to stroll into a bar or sashay on to a dance-floor for the entire female company to fall at their feet. Women melt, but never for me.

But it is all going to change. Because if I want to spend January nights in my own bed rather than in the frosty stock-yard, somehow I am going to have to learn how to turn on the charm. It is all to do with the sheep.

It is time for the lusty old ram to tup his ewes and, if last year's performance is anything to go by, it is going to be a long drawn-out affair. In an ideal world, he would only have to be in the field for a couple of weeks – the frequency of the ewe's fertility cycle – and within that short time every sheep would come on heat at least once. Providing the old chap had not been keeping late nights, there is no reason why he should not accomplish his passionate task within fourteen days. But last year it took him nearly two months to get round them all. I know that because the first lambs were born the second week in January and the last few in March. That is a lot of cold nights for this shepherd to be out of doors.

I blamed the ram, calling him an idle swine and publicly doubting his masculinity; but now I must apologise, for it may have been the girls who were at fault. As I now understand it, although ewes come into season naturally, a bit of a kick-start is not a bad idea. Imagine a flock of sheep on a dance-floor and the only chap present a regular old-timer known to one and all. Familiarity has bred contempt, and those ewes could bop around all night without a single romantic thought crossing their woolly heads. But wait! Suppose a newcomer bursts on the scene: a big lad fresh from his motor-bike, the musky scent of sweat rising from his tight leathers. You'd have a dance-floor inflamed with such passion that the fire-brigade might have to be called in. And – here is the clever bit – even the old boy in the corner might start to look attractive. This is exactly the effect I need to create.

To achieve it, I was thinking of using a teaser ram. This is a sheep who has all his masculinity about him but has had a vasectomy. The effect is quite simple. He gets the ewes steaming away over a period of a couple of weeks, and then the ram proper is introduced to the flock. By then the ewes are aroused to fever pitch and after a couple of weeks the old ram is presumably stretchered off the field, mission accomplished.

I was discussing this plan with our sheep-shearer but having pressed his nose deep into the fleece of the prospective teaser, he doubted there was enough smell. 'You want one o' them stinking old mountain breeds with a bit o' smell to 'em. These lowland breeds haven't really got it.' This caused me to rethink my plans. The vasectomy is an expensive operation and if the teaser is going to be lacking in the raunchy perfume department then the whole thing could be a waste of time.

Then, as we were shearing the big ram, a casual remark set me thinking. I was admiring the quality of the pure white fleece and mentioned that I might have it spun and knitted into a heavy winter sweater. The clippers went silent. 'I wouldn't if I was you. Smell, you see, when it gets wet. Smells something 'orrid. Really rammy. That's how it smells. Real rammy.'

So that's the solution! Buy a fleece from a rank, stench-stewed old mountain ram; find a knitter with a failing nose and at the first sign of rain, stroll gently into the field of ewes. With luck, the odour would catalyse the situation more potently than Chanel ever imagined a perfume could. Needless to say, I would make a tactical withdrawal if things got out of hand. Just look at what I would have achieved if I had known about this in time. The ewes all on heat like a field of electric fires, a sweater to keep me warm, and pounds saved on the vet's bill.

And for the first time in my life, all the girls would be looking for me.

P LEASE DO NOT accuse me of being lazy when I tell you that this year we have hired a machine to dig out the over-wintered muck in the horse-yard. Last year we did the job with a horse and tumbril. But this year I couldn't, for two good reasons.

The first is that having had an intensive week of gathering the hay and building the hay-stack, I now find that I have developed a complete aversion to pitch-forks. I only have to see one lying in the corner of the barn for my legs to itch the way they do after a long session in midge-laden hay. I also break out into the same dampening sweat that overpowers me as I fork bundle after bundle of dried grass high on to the waggon in an atmosphere so hot and humid that I might as well be farming in a pressure cooker. So I am chickening out.

The other reason is that last year I had the company of an amiable visiting Quaker who laced each working hour with inspiring reflection, and whose enthusiasm to dig his fork ever deeper and fling the muck ever higher was fed in some way by his inner peace of mind. I have never seen a happier man on the end of a fork. Alas, he is not around this year and the thought of three days up to the knees in muck with less inspiring company (of which there is plenty) did not appeal. The digger arrives on Monday.

But I shall not be present and watching. To organic farmers who waste not and want not, the composting of muck is a great display of faith, and the hauling of it from the yards a significant sacrament. I shall be observing the digger driver, and if I find he is not taking the job seriously or making ribald comments, I shall have him off the farm and the horse between the shafts before you can say 'G'up!'

But if you are not a muck-lover then I doubt that any words of mine will convert you. I could describe to you the dankness and the fibrous texture of it when it is at its very best; when the smell is pungent but not obnoxious and the colour as rich as purest chocolate. It has a life-force of its own, does muck, which makes it sing on the end of the tines. It is at its worst if wet and flowing, more like stew than sponge cake; then the smell is rank and sharp and as the dollops fly through the air they are to be avoided for they give off devastating blobs of depressingly filthy liquid that will be with you a week if one happens to fall on your lips.

But despite the odd drawbacks, once a muck-man always a muck-man. I have read recently of the vendor of a minor stately home who was happy to leave his mansion but did not finally go till he had removed the muck-heap. The Prince of Wales is a mucky sort, too. He has been publicly speaking on the need for cities to compost their muck rather than waste it. The end-product could then be used to revitalise the hungry soil that intensive farming has beaten into submission.

So perhaps the time is right for some really dirty talk. I am indebted to David Stickland, an eminent organicist, for a filthy solution to an increasingly pressing problem. It is now becoming apparent that the recently negotiated reforms to the Common Agricultural Policy will not reduce surplus production in the long run – farmers and scientists are simply too clever. Tell them to farm less land (they are being told to put 15 per cent into set-aside) and the farmer simply farms even more intensively on the land he is left with, aided by the scientists developing ever more abundant crops. You are soon back where you started.

Stickland's idea goes like this. Instead of offering cash not to use land, offer a subsidy to farmers who make use of organic fertilisers: subsidy would help because the trouble with ordure is that it is like an elderly relation who insists on travelling first class, expensive and troublesome to move around. Yet if we could organise ourselves into getting it cheaply from where there is excess of it – the towns – out to the fields where organic matter is in desperately short supply, then everyone would be happy. It seems to me verging on the criminal for tons of organic matter to be tipped, buried and forgotten. A well-mucked field is a healthy field – even the most intensive of growers do not deny it. I commend action on this to our Mr Gummer who could yet make British farming history. And headlines, too, though at least one would no doubt read 'Gummer Hits the Fan!' But we must all suffer for organic principle. I have done my bit. Now it is his turn.

I HAVE CONTRACTED an infectious disease. I have grave suspicions that I caught it from the sheep. The symptoms are disturbing: you suddenly find yourself walking with a jaunty gait as if everything were well with the world; a song appears on your lips and a smile on your face where all winter has been a weary frown. Instead of worrying about what disasters may befall the budding crops, you see only how well the land looks, how straight the furrows. Songwriters would call it love; but the sheep and I know it is something different.

It is nothing to do with the weather. In fact, after a deliciously mild spell we are once again raked by icy northerly winds that make cows and horses defiantly turn their backs in that direction. But despite the chill, an unmistakable feeling of elation is on us.

The sheep sensed it a couple of weeks before I did; and the little lambs sniffed it even before their experienced mothers. Yet it took two days of liberation from the lambing pens before the symptoms first appeared. Sheep do not like change, and even though they were freed from the enclosure of the farm-yard and put out to grass they still bleated pitifully to be brought home at night in the hope that delicious food might be laid before them in troughs. But lying at their feet was a rich feast, finer than any bucket could carry. The spring grass was shooting forth with vigour: packed with nourishment, if only they realised it. It would have been easy to have succumbed to their pleadings and brought them home had I not remembered a great truth I discovered tucked away in a shepherd's memoirs. 'Sheep', he said, 'are not stupid. They just need time to think.' So I gave them time, and soon they were tucking in enthusiastically.

The effect of the grass on the lambs was dramatic. Made healthily plump by a rush of revitalised milk, they bounded round the field as if propelled by elastic bands. First they ran this way and that; and then, presumably having had time to think about it, decided it would be more fun to run a race. So began the Lambs' Grand National which seems to have its starting line somewhere near the trough and finishes eight acres away near the gate. Some just ran, others leaped along like liberated kangaroos and others, drunk on mother's milk, flung themselves into the air with such vigour that they landed facing the other way and fled backwards. It took them a long time to think that one through.

But my own feeling of well-being comes as much from the look of the land as from the antics of the lambs. We are now beginning our second full year and all the plans which we have worked so hard to accomplish are gradually paying off. Like the meadow on which the lambs frolic: I sowed the seed this time last year and watched its feeble attempts to grow as it took successive assaults from frost and, worse, drought. It never really grew at all last summer, merely raising sad wisps of fragile green that were never destined to flourish. The weakness of the grass was matched only by the strength of the weeds, and by the middle of the year I had a fine meadow of thistles, poppies, mayweed, nettles and docks. But no grass.

I was on the point of giving up, ploughing the field, and consigning the notion of organic growing to the back-burner. After all, had I wanted to apply chemicals to kill the weeds and fertilise the grass, I could easily have done so. Instead, I took advice from one of my aged farming text-books, and merely took the mower to it. The horses and I dragged that rackety old mower up and down for the best part of two days and then turned our back on the field, not even bothering to clear what we had cut. The weeds once more took hold, the grass maintained its modesty. I checked the text-book once again, and when the horses gave me a cold stare, asked a friend to do the second round with his tractor.

By mid September the magic started to work. The weeds had vanished, the grass had woken from its unnaturally long slumber. Back from the grave it is now as green and thick as the Wembley turf, with hardly a weed in sight.

Is it any wonder that I am cheered, not only to see success snatched from the jaws of disaster, but to have the young lambs joining in the celebration? Add to that the contented cows who are sniffing the air and dreaming of days soon out at pasture; and the hard-working horses still shuffling around winter's strawed yards, but looking forward to their first mouthful of the scented grass they helped to grow.

Grass is springing and our spirits are high. If only the cart-horses and I could work out a way of harvesting that feeling and packing it in sacks, our fortunes would be made.

T HERE IS A PRACTICE among the older generation of farm-workers which is known as 'squaring-up'. It occurs when a free-ranging mind connects with idle limbs to carry out some indefinite purpose. So one might wander to the hay-stack with a pitch-fork and 'just square-it-up'. It would not be a tiring or geo-metrical operation; merely the flicking of wisps of hay with appar-ently little point other than the satisfaction of the man on the end of the fork. The hay-stack looks no better at the end of it but it is squared-up, and the man happier.

I only mention this because I have been squaring-up my farming diary and it has been published in a book.* I fear I cannot bring myself to read it. The memories are still too raw. I do not want to be reminded of the day the cows invaded a swimming-pool, or various shaming incidents involving what my wife calls 'those

* *Farming Times* (H. F. & G. Witherby 1992).

woolly bastards'. Nor the state of hysteria I reached after growing tons of oats and finding myself unable to turn them into one bowl of porridge. Or the day – all right, several days – when we tried to catch the wild bullock that had lived a lonely life on the marsh and saw no reason to re-enter society. As for the binder, why should I be forced to think of it out of season? Perish the thought. No, this is not a book for me. But do not let me put you off. I have many mouths to feed and sugar-beet nuts do not grow on trees.

So I am going to have to indulge in publicity, hit the headlines and get myself talked about. I thought I might persuade this news-paper to sponsor one of their distinguished public debates and have been searching my soul for a burning issue. Alas, I find the only thing on my mind is whether I should lift the mangel-wurzels this week, or leave them till next and risk a frost in favour of more growth. 'This House believes the Mangels should be Lifted Now!' is hardly going to bring Fay Weldon and Lord St John to their feet.

So I have been looking to other authors to see how they manage hype and I have been greatly impressed by a blonde pop-star called Madonna. She has removed her famous corset and posed for photo-graphs which leave little even to the dullest of imaginations (and which look, I have to say, terribly familiar to anyone acquainted with the mating rituals of the farm-yard). Since there is talk of her book being banned and there is nothing like prohibition for promoting sales, perhaps it would work for me? Hold on to your hats; here it comes.

This week I am going to talk about breasts. We have had some cracking breasts on the farm this week. Long ones, pencil-slim ones with delicate curves, some short and rather bulky ones, and a rare one that has been worn thin by regular use. Another is so massive that I cannot see how a man could handle it at all. Still, variety is the spice of life and during the course of the last week I have handled them all, got the feel of them under my rough, horny hands. How am I doing? Steamy stuff, eh?

These glistening, provocative breasts belong to my plough and I have been working my way through them with a view to finding one that will give me the edge in next week's ploughing match. I never knew there was so much to a plough breast. It is an apparently simple curved sheet of iron that inverts the soil as it slides over; but its apparent simplicity hides the poetry of perfect motion, for if the ploughman looks briefly away from his horses and furrow, he will see that the breast of the plough is no mere bully, coarsely pushing the land aside. The breast nudges the soil, presses and rolls it with the deft gentleness of a chef turning pastry. Long thin breasts are the finest because of the slowness with which they turn the soil leaving the furrows unbroken. But a harder, more stubborn land needs a firmer touch and a short, brutal breast deals best with it. You can get obsessed with breasts: when I am alone in my study with the wife away, I like to leaf through old plough catalogues from the 1890s, reading about drag chains, wrought iron welded bodies and chilled breast linings. Sometimes I lie in the bath and think about Hornsby's Patent Self-Lifting Arrangement for hours. Is that enough smut to get me condemned and sold by the million? I hope so, for I can think of no other way of drawing attention to this book. Not now that the Booker dinner is over and someone else has got the Nobel. The publisher did have another suggestion but, quite frankly, pictures of me wearing corsets and a ram-harness are not going to do anybody a favour.

U NTIL LAST WEEKEND I never thought it was possible for a pig to grin. Pigs' moods are easy to determine by listening to their grunts, which will be low and rumbling if in a conversational mood, or high-pitched and piercing if tetchy. But never in my experience does a pig have a facial expression. However, last Saturday night, I am certain that, for possibly the first time in anthropological history, I saw a pig beam.

It is because we held our annual Potato-picking Weekend in which we invite the general public to follow our horses along the furrow, bending and plucking from the soil succulent organic spuds. Cunning wheeze, eh? Not only does it save me the trouble of having to pick them myself which, with our aged machinery, is a slow, back-breaking and expensive business (teams of pickers have to be paid), but it gives an opportunity for those who have never seen cart-horses at work or plunged their hands into soil to get stuck in. Children sink to their wellington tops in the mud and hold contests to see who can find the largest potato. The tiniest merely stand and gaze at the Suffolk Punches and, when they have come to terms with this overpowering presence, brave themselves to ask what the horses are called.

But the adults are the most entertaining. At any given moment you will see one man with a camcorder. In his mind he is remaking *Far From the Madding Crowd*, but in reality it is not even likely to make the Jeremy Beadle show. Then there are the devotional green-minded ones who bend and pick with religious fervour, giving thanks for the rich smells of the freshly turned soil and handling each picked potato as if it were a miracle in itself. And we get others who will mutter, 'My old dad grew taters. He wouldn't think much of these little uns,' as they fling aside a cannonball of a spud.

Back in the farm-yard, a trusty team of neighbours mans the scales and herds the crowd towards the farm shop. Once there, they have to confront my wife who, it has to be said, is more at home at her desk than bending over a freezer being quizzed about the difference between rolled rib and topside. But she bravely plays the part of the farmer's wife, only balking at questions such as 'Hey, didn't *you* used to be something or other before you worked here?' Strange how many people get a frozen hunk of brisket dropped on their toes.

So what is there in all this to cause the pigs to grin? The answer is the weather: potato-picking, for those who are not being paid to do it, is a fair-weather pastime. After one dry and bright day the forecast was for torrential rain. I had decided that if it came, and we couldn't clear the entire field, I would not bother to pick the potatoes that remained. Prices are so low that it is barely economic to unearth them. But they would not go to waste, for that most efficient of potato-lifters, the pig's snout, would finish the job for me. I would turn the pigs on to the field and they could spend from now till Christmas in a nutritional treasure hunt. Word of this plan reached them and as the storm clouds gathered the piggies began to grin.

Hoping for better weather than forecast we prepared for the second day, deciding to offer cups of tea and a traditional Suffolk bun called 'fourses'. These are a heavy blend of flour, egg, lard and currants, described by my aged recipe book as 'filling'. It is said that ploughmen took them to the field on harsh winter days. The ones we made were better suited to propping up the legs of wobbly tables. Imagine scones cast in plaster-of-paris and you get the picture. One old lady took one look and said, 'Mmm. I remember them. Of course, we were poor in those days. We had to eat things like that.' Alas, we had made two hundred.

To the credit of our customers, the weather did not deter them. In lashing rain they slopped along the furrows, wiping the mud from their hands on the grassy headland, applauding the horses who were having to pull with all their might to get the potato machine through the sodden soil.

And as basket after basket was taken from the fields, the pigs grew ever more gloomy as they saw meal by meal disappear into paper sacks. They lined up at the fence and gazed despairingly as the last ridge was lifted. 'Never mind,' I cried to the pigs, 'it's fourses all round for tea.'

Not only can pigs grin. They can sneer, too.

M OST AMATEUR WRITERS dream that one day they will produce a tale that will propel them up the best-seller lists. I suspect that most small farmers also imagine that, lurking within them, is a scheme which will turn their tiny farms into gold mines. They might invent a new crop, like ornamental marrows; or something so natural and rustic that it is irresistible, like organic socks. I know an inventive fellow who turned a tidy shilling from selling pumpkins to American servicemen who were stationed nearby, but his brief seasonal selling spree was too short to sustain him through the year. Another local farmer has tried sweaters knitted in goat wool; we have had dried-flower farms and corn-dolly factories. But although they start with a flourish of optimism, pass by a year later and the sign is still hanging by the farm gate with the paint peeling and the squeaking hinge singing the death-song of another hopeful enterprise.

Nevertheless, I am taking my commercial life in my hands and, deliberately refusing to learn from others' mistakes, I am launching on a project which will have the grocery trade queuing down the lane for what I have to offer.

I was walking past the corn-stacks and idly wondering what to do with the wheat. Our wheat is different from most wheat grown these days for it came from an old variety of seed known as Squarehead's Master. I grew it with a view to saving its precious long straw either to sell to a thatcher who would treasure it, or to use on the farm to thatch our own hay-stacks and lambing sheds. The wheat, I had decided, would be ground up to feed the pigs. But I decided to do a little research and found among my aged farming tomes that, in its day, this wheat was much prized for bread-making. Like Bell at the moment he thought of the telephone or Archimedes of his Principle, I was consumed with a half-formed idea. Here was this wheat: it was grown on an organic farm where the land had been ploughed with horses; Suffolk Punches had hauled the seed drill and planted it in the ground, hoed the crop and carted it to the stack. From there it was fed – by characters who could be straight out of Hardy – into a venerable threshing machine. If this wheat were made into flour, somehow, would it not pack every rural cliché that a romantic could muster?

Carried along by enthusiasm, I decided to search for a marketing name. I cannot command the genius that came up with Homepride but I understand the principle. Surely my bags of flour emblazoned with potent rural images should do the same.

I was half-way to ordering a Mercedes motor-car on the imagined profits when a letter in the post halted me in my tracks. The letter was from a miller enquiring if we could supply him with organic grain. But he was no ordinary miller. He works the only remaining mill in East Anglia to be powered solely by the wind. It sits on the marshes where Suffolk meets Norfolk and after a gruelling restoration project is once again grinding wheat into flour between its mighty stones. My chest tightened as I read his note and I imagined my bags of flour proudly boasting, 'An Ancient Seed, Grown with Horse-power, Matured in Genuine Thatched Ricks, Sworn at in Dialect, Now Milled by the Wind!' I could see the packets lining the shelves at Fortnum and Mason and crowding every National Trust gift-shop. Make that two Mercs.

But before I went any further, I thought I ought to check that the wheat is up to the job. As it is still standing safely in the cornstack, in order to have enough for a baking experiment I swept up a pound or two of grains that had fallen from the sheaves as they had been pitched on to the waggon. Some were a bit mouldy, others dirty and there was distinct evidence that a mouse or two had passed that way; but I optimistically bunged them into our brutal electric hammer mill that normally smashes barley for the pigs.

I will not describe the resulting dust, except that I would not presume to call it flour. It was the grittiness, coupled with the faint odour of rodent, that decided me not to progress further. But I am not downcast. I am taking steps to secure a somewhat cleaner sample for the jolly miller. In the meantime the Merc is on hold.

ALONE AMONG THOSE who follow the saga of the troubled marriage of the Prince and Princess of Wales, I am in a position to make certain disclosures which may explain their gloom. I know it seems unlikely that a mere farmer should hit upon the truth when the skilled professional royal-watchers have given it their undivided attention: but they spend too much time peering through telephoto lenses when they would be better scanning the small print of the agricultural journals. Therein they will discover the real reason that the Waleses are having a tiff.

It is because he is a farmer. And it matters not one jot that he is the second highest person in the land, his farm is probably going down the pan as fast as every other one in Britain. Cuts in subsidies, environment pressures, Brussels regulations, wet harvests – farmers, believe me, get edgy and their wives fed up with the constant complaining. Everyone has suffered and no farmer can pull rank. There is only one solution, we are repeatedly told. Diversify! Be inventive and come up with new ideas for using your land and your crops!

Well, the Prince of Wales has come up with a cracking idea and, by strange coincidence, a similar one crossed my mind at roughly the same time; and I can tell you that since then the incidence of marital frost in this household has greatly increased. He has my sympathy.

His idea was to take his surplus oats and wheat and bake the mixture into biscuits, and then stamp on each one his own insignia – the three feathers – and since he is not as skint as most farmers sell them in aid of charity. This is a classic example of what farmers are being urged to do. As diversification ideas go, it takes the biscuit.

My idea was to do with pigs. There is little profit in fattening pigs and sending them to market if you farm on a small scale as we do. Anyway, butchers do not like our black pigs and I do not care for their livestock markets so there is little chance of a profitable marriage there. Therefore we have been turning pigs into joints of pork locally, selling them from the farm and making a modest shilling that way. But not quite enough shillings, so I decided to take the idea one step further and add even more value to the pigs by turning them into sausages. Not having an heraldic stamp of my own to place upon the pack, I decided that they should be our village's own sausage, with a portion of the proceeds going towards a fund to restore the church bells to the belfry. To ensure democracy and create interest, I decided that the village would hold an election and, from three differently flavoured sausages on offer, vote for one to carry the village's name. That was the easy bit.

The scene now changes to the kitchen where I found myself confronted with a plastic bag full of pigs' intestines, which the butcher assured me were easy to handle, an attachment to the food-mixer which squirted the sausagemeat into the guts, and a row of herbs and spices. Like Farmer Jekyll, I started to mix my brew.

I imagine there were similar scenes at Highgrove as the Prince got out his Kenwood Chef and put on his apron to create the perfect, personal biscuit. I wonder if he got the same mocking from his spouse that I did. Did he have to suffer his family filing past his efforts and muttering 'yuk'? My skins oozed their fillings as my farmer's fingers and thumbs proved too hefty to tie tidy little knots on the ends of the sausages. The family shrank back.

And what happened at Highgrove when it came to the tasting? I offered my own princess my exciting blend of pig-meat, bread-crumbs and herbs and waited for a radiant beam to cross her face. All I got was a withering look worthy of Queen Mary. 'Look, darling,' I cried, 'I am only doing this for the farm!' An outburst that could well have come from either of our farmhouse kitchens. As I flung more herbs into the mixer, festooned intestine around the kitchen like Christmas streamers and scowled at the wife, I pondered what a snooper with a long lens would make of our facial expressions.

So the next time you open the newspaper and see a frosty Royal expression, give it the benefit of the doubt. It could be simply that he has run up half a pound of his latest organic oat-and-nasturtium cookies and is getting a less than enthusiastic response. Here, after working through sausages with garlic and paprika, gin and juniper berry, sage and black pepper, our marriage is rocked to its foundations. If my wife had even the slightest pretext to head for Paris alone, she undoubtedly would.

O F THE SMALL FARMERS that I have met, there are few to whom the notion of a holiday is not entirely foreign. They do not sit in their tractor-cabs dreaming of Venice; they are not forever harbouring wistful thoughts of the Seychelles as they muck out the pig sty. And even if they do manage to drag themselves away for a couple of days, they spend the entire time tortured with thoughts of what might be happening back home. In this way they are quite correct. I am convinced that my stock plan their demise to occur only during my brief absences. I sometimes think they are tapping my phone, and if they ever hear me making a hotel reservation the cattle, sheep and pigs get together and draw straws to decide whose death is most likely to cause me the greatest guilt. I have come to expect it. Although I leave impeccably responsible people in charge, whenever I get back from a weekend the first tool I reach for is the spade.

So how do small farmers ever get a break? The answer is that they only ever leave their farms for the company of other farmers, at events where any guilt is diluted by the notion that the next man in the beer tent is even more fretful than you. Last weekend I went on a busman's holiday. You might not think that I could derive any pleasure whatsoever from taking my horses to plough on a traditional farm, with Large Black pigs like we have at home and even Red Poll cattle. But this was different, and I am now beginning to see that the man who drives the 47 bus could indeed find complete relaxation in steering the number 85.

Every year, in September, the owners of Suffolk Punch cart-horses gather for what has become known as their Spectacular. It has none of the fierce competitive edge of an agricultural show. It is more of a clan gathering, a thanksgiving for the greatest cart-horse in the world.

For our farm it has become a works outing. Dilly arrived early in the morning with his sandwiches and wearing his suit. Derek arrived in hob-nailed boots, for he could no more plough without hob-nails than a guardsman could protect the Queen without a busby on. Star and Blue clattered up the ramp of the lorry in the dawn and the cheery little band hit the road, heading for the Norfolk Museum of Rural Life traditional working farm.

Although my little band of farmworkers have known each other for only a couple of years, we behave with the predictability of aged married couples. Dilly always asks how the mangels are. I tell him they are fine. He then tells us that in his day they only used to grow four: 'One in each corner of the field, and roll 'em home!' We know it is coming. But we laugh, loud and long. Then Derek says that it'll be too dry to plough right, and we all agree.

On the showground we meet old friends. Dilly has an acquaintance who lives a mere two miles from his home but whom he only ever sees once a year at the Spectacular. Derek bumped into a man with whom he last farmed in 1945. 'What was his name?' I asked. 'I don't know,' said Derek.

Names do not matter here. I have been ploughing at these events for long enough now to be on comradely terms with men whose names and home counties I do not know. We stand at the headland and finish interrupted conversations from the year before; and all the time, eyes of old men blaze with a forgotten fire at the sight of a Suffolk Punch and plough. We turn the soil at a pedestrian pace; horses are eyed up and down, breath drawn sharply inwards at the sight of some of them, admiration heaped on others. The spectators sit around on bales of straw. The commentator exchanges banter with a heckler. 'Shuurrup and ger' on with it,' cries the good-natured old lady. 'I'm sorry,' replies the man with the microphone, 'a lady over there is making such a terrible noise, she seems to have swallowed a chicken bone.' You don't get that sort of wit at Royal Ascot. Over on the other side of the field, the sheaf-tossing competition is reaching its climax and the man who has been trying to run the terrier-racing promises it will work better next year.

And we have been ploughing slowly and talking much. Phone numbers have been exchanged, secret intelligence on the where-abouts of a share for a Ransome's semi-digger plough has been gathered. And by the time the horses are clattering their weary way back up the lorry ramp we are all ready for home. Dilly asks how the mangels are. Derek says it ploughed better than he thought. By the time the hooves and hob-nails crunch across the yard it is dark. 'How are things?' I ask nervously. 'Fine,' replies my wife. Good, I think. All hearts on the farm beating satisfactorily. As were ours.

I T HAS BEEN a black week but a happy one, and much of my pleasure has been due to a reader of this column. Some weeks ago, I wrote of my longing to own a shepherd's hut; a little house on wheels in which shepherds would dwell at lambing time, watching over their flocks by night. I imagined it with a spartan bunk and a cheery billy-stove to give warmth to both shepherd and sickly lambs during the chilly nights. It would have a double door so the top half could be opened for fresh air, but the bottom remain closed for cosiness. Perhaps there might be room in it for an old leather chair in which I could doze and again imagine myself as Hardy's hero shepherd, Gabriel Oak, tending my flock of Dorset sheep. I could hear the crackle of the kindling, the sing of the kettle, the beat of the rain on the tiny windows as the hut rocked gently in the stormy winds. But most of those huts were built of timber and, having fallen redundant, were allowed to rot. To be honest, I never expected to find one.

I did not reckon upon Farmer Payne of Essex who retires this week. He wrote to tell me that he has been the proud owner of just such a hut. I fled south with the speed of a cow escaping a warble-fly and found, lying in his farm-yard, the hut of my dreams. It is big and black. It oozes preserving black tar and atmosphere, and is as sound as the day the builder, Mr G. Candy of Roxwell, proudly screwed his nameplate above the door. No sooner had it taken its place on our farm than it started to work its magic.

It so happened that I had decided that the day on which the hut was due was also the day that the sheep should have their feet trimmed. Sheep are naturally mountain animals and would wear away their hooves in the normal course of scrabbling over rocks. Ambling round meadows does not have the same abrasive effect, so the shepherd has to do the toe-nail cutting for them.

Having eased the precious hut off its transporter, settled it into position, admired it and made plans for the stove, I went to the top of the farm to gather the sheep.

They looked a fine sight from afar, washed white by the recent heavy rains and set against the vivid green of the sprouting spring grass. The lambs frolicked, the old ewes kept their heads down, grazing, raising their eyes only to check that I was no threat to their offspring. Except one ewe. She lay helplessly on her back, twitching, legs in the air, stomach distended to the point of bursting. Her eyes rolled, mouth frothed. She had bloat. Bloat is caused by a build-up of gas in the sheep, due either to overeating or to the ewe having rolled accidentally on to her back and not been able to get the right way up. In such a position, sheep are unable to expel gases and can quickly die. A shepherd must act quickly.

The hut having cast its nostalgic spell, with Gabriel Oak on my mind, I remembered the dramatic scene in *Far From the Madding Crowd* when a whole flock was found 'swollen with wind' on clover. 'Gabriel was already among the turgid prostrate forms. He flung off his coat, rolled up his shirt-sleeves, and took from his pocket the instrument of salvation . . .'

He was a braver man than I am, for what he held in his hand was a lance with which to pierce the sheep's rumen and allow the gases to escape. Fine if you hit the right spot, deadly if you miss. Turning my back on tradition I took the easier route and ran to the kitchen, poured a cup of cooking oil, and having hauled the sheep to her feet, poured it down her throat. I have been told this never fails and the only precaution the shepherd must take is to stand well back for the accumulated gases can make a rapid exit from both ends at once.

In fact, it gushed with such vigour that it woke my other piece of black-but-happy news. Alice, the Large Black sow, is once again in her sty and about to farrow. She raised her snout to sniff the shepherd's hut as it trundled by and gave a dismissive *Hrr-oink!* She knows from experience that sheep get all the blooming attention round here and it is highly probable that when her time comes, she will merely nestle down and deliver her litter in silence and without fuss. She fears, too, that now the farmer has a cosy nest of his own and a stove over which to play shepherds, the swill bucket will be even later in arriving. Hrr-oink!

35

2
New Loves
(And an Old Friend Goes)

T HIS WEEK I have been wandering the farm humming the old Beatles song, 'Can't Buy Me Love'. It has been proved cruelly true.

What happened was that things have come finally to a head after two long years of struggling with cattle. Either, I said, I am going to have to find a cow with whom I can develop a relationship; or give up the whole idea of keeping cattle on this farm. With the cart-horses, pigs and sheep I sense clearly that not only am I happy to keep them, they are content to be farmed by me. So why do the cattle always hate me so?

You will probably be only too well aware of my patchy career as a stockman, and may recall past moments of horror. These range from the message left by my telephone, 'Your cows have been in our swimming pool!' to the great escape of the calf Ronnie Biggs, and the demise of one particular cow so unstable that my neighbour, on first seeing her, took one look at her rolling eyes and asked whether she also breathed fire. And he is a cowman by profession. My cattle career had reached its crossroads. I had to do something.

Strangely, I was given a sign. My wife had been talking to a cattle breeder who had sung the praises of one particular breed, and at the very same time as she was telling me this my eye fell upon an advertisement for the self-same breed. It boasted, 'Easy calving, docile, good-natured'. I decided that the British White, reputed to be the oldest breed of cattle in Britain, was the breed for me. It also has the advantage of being as white as a sheet, with the exception of the ears, nose and teats which are velvety black. I have always had red cows, but as I am colour-blind I have suffered many heart-stopping moments of glancing across the meadow and finding the cows have disappeared. They turn out to be standing against a green hedge. So the lighthouse effect of a white cow sounded very promising.

This time, I approached my cattle-buying in a hardly commercial

39

frame of mind. I was not interested in carcass weights, feed conversion ratios, pedigrees or championships. I wanted a cow that liked me, and I was prepared to pay for it. If it took money to buy me love, so be it.

I viewed a magnificent herd of British White cattle not far away. Drifting through them like a balloonist crossing snowy Alps, I gasped at the glacial might of the bull, Alfred, and made overtures to every cow in turn. 'This one is in calf to the champion . . .' they would boast, but I was not interested. 'Is it friendly?' I asked. If they were not sure we passed on. Cow after cow failed the affection test, until one, a looming iceberg of an animal called Sage, detached herself from the herd and ambled in our direction. A cow that heads towards me voluntarily is the sort of cow for me. I asked for more details. She was an experienced mother, having given four good calves; yes, she was very friendly – and no, she was not for sale as she was due to calve in October.

I looked her in the eye, even reached out to stroke the sooty blackness of her nose. Sage did not flinch, but bowed her head respectfully and licked my boots. I put my arms around her neck as a final test, and declared her to be the cow for me. I paid a good price to compensate for disrupting the farmer's breeding routine. Money, I thought, had bought me love.

She arrived last week and soon settled with the small herd; only the sheep took some time to adjust, never having seen a white cow before. As she walked towards the flock, they stood transfixed by her radiance, as if a Messiah had come among them. Visitors to the farm stroked her and had their boots licked and I thought my cow-keeping troubles were over.

But last night, with a strong wind blowing, I strolled up to see her. She saw me approach but did not make towards me as she had on our first date. I inched closer and she looked round, plotting an escape route as cows do when cornered. I cooed her name and she swished her tail. I called to her softly and her eyes merely widened. Then she fled; slowly at first but gathering speed as I neared her. 'You faithless cow!' I cried like a sugar-daddy betrayed. 'You two-timer! Do you know how much I paid for you?' My heart was broken. We were back to the bad old days of shouting at cows. Money can't buy you love. Was it the wind that spooked her, or was she deceiving me all along? I shall go again tomorrow and report.

T HIS WEEK I grasped one last bite of the summer before autumn took over. Like a man clutching at the last of the falling blossom and hoping to capture the spring, I took the horses and mower to the field of lucerne and made hay. Mid-September is not the normal hay-making season but lucerne (sometimes called alfalfa) is a generous crop which has given us three harvests this year. I have read that some years she will give four. But it is not for her generosity that I admire her, it is her scent. The perfume of the lucerne when it has been cut and allowed to wilt in a desiccating north-westerly breeze has a seductive quality that Parisian perfumiers would be hard pressed to match.

At least, that is how I felt about it on Friday. On Saturday it rained, and the lucerne became just another sodden, mucky mass. That, I have found, is traditional farming. Romance one minute and a slap in the face the next.

But this is by the way, compared with the news you are eagerly expecting on the developing relationship between me and our new white cow, Sage. I have already poured out my broken heart about how, despite lavishing generous sums of money to buy a cow with which I could develop a working relationship, things got off on the wrong foot. My approaches were met with indifference, my offers of comradeship spurned. Even a bucket of sugar-beet nuts (the equivalent of giving a girl a good dinner in the hope of a goodnight kiss) was spurned. I rashly promised further reports.

Well, you are not going to get any. It has become all too clear that public scrutiny is no help in healing shaky relationships; too easy to read false truths into brief glimpses of other people's lives. For example, I brought her into the farm-yard a couple of days ago for testing by the Ministry's vet. I managed to slip a halter on her and lead her down the farm. Had you seen us on this formal public occasion you might have thought we were the happiest couple in the world. Yet ten minutes later as I released her from her capture, she slid out a rear foot with the clear intention of giving me a hefty kick. Had you caught only that moment in your telephoto lens, you would have a story about our union being heavily on the rocks. Neither picture is entirely true so I beg to be left in peace for a while.

I do not know if it is the whiteness of the new cow that has inspired me, but I have decided to discover the joys of whitewash and spruce up the stable, which can get rather gloomy in the dark winter days. I could easily have opted for a nice tin of Dulux, but as you will be well aware we never do anything the easy way here. Anyway, whitewash is a quarter the price and from an artistic point of view has an instant antique texture that no modern paint can match. I discovered it is made by dangerously mixing hydrated lime and water, during which process great heat is produced. This is then used to allow tallow, or candle-wax, to be melted into the white slop to give it elasticity. I was about to set up a witch's cauldron and mix a gallon or two when a visitor told me of a man who sells it ready-mixed, in tins. It comes with a health warning. 'It can sting can this stuff,' he told me. 'I found that out the hard way, I did.' He fingered the zip on his trousers and grimaced.

Wearing gloves, and forgoing my morning gallon of tea in case I should accidentally repeat his stinging experience, I slapped away till I resembled the white cow myself. Then, ghostlike, I ambled round the corner to where the young Large Black sow, Phoebe, had given birth to ten piglets some hours before. All was well; ten silky black babies, each secured to a teat and sucking like vacuum cleaners at their mother's milk. It occurred to me that Alice, Phoebe's mother, should be told the news of the birth. She is easily upset if events pass her by. Plastered in whitewash I stumbled to the orchard and broke the news. There was a grunt which I took to mean, 'Rejoice, rejoice. We are a grandmother.' And there you have it. The latest news from this farm – in black and white. At least, all the news that's fit to print.

New Loves (And an Old Friend Goes)

As I write, I stand at the foothills of the last peak to be scaled before I can truly call myself a traditional farmer. I have harnessed horses and learned to plough, lambed sheep, grown corn and built hay-stacks. But I have never milked a cow. My first victim is standing in the yard, blissfully unaware that an amateurish pair of hands is about to assault her most delicate and providing parts.

This was not at all what I had planned. On Saturday a local farmer retired and held an auction of his lifetime's farming possessions. I planned a late breakfast, a quick fling of the swill at the pigs and the rest of the day spent in gentle bidding. The cow decided otherwise.

As I rounded the corner of the barn heading for the pigs, heavy swill buckets in each hand, I glanced across to the cow meadow as I do every morning and counted the stock. There should be three red blobs, the Red Poll cattle, and one radiant white beacon, Sage, the British White cow. But the corner of my eye caught not one white blob but two. The first was Sage, the other no more than a white smudge among the grass. I reassured myself that it could not possibly be her calf, which was not due for three more weeks; but feeling uneasy I strode across the field to inspect what I hoped would turn out to be a stray fertiliser bag that had drifted along on the breeze.

As I got nearer it was clear that this was no rubbish; this was a calf with the merest grasp on life. The cow licked it and nudged it but it did not rise to its feet or open its eyes. It breathed with a rasping gasp. I ran back to the house, mind racing, and tried to ring my network of local advisers. Alas, they were all at the farm sale, except faithful Dilly who said he would miss the first few items to give me a hand.

I lifted the calf, which was heavy despite its pathetic limpness, and summoning all my strength carried it across the meadow towards the farm-yard. Sage followed, anxious and mooing for her new-born son. I carried him half the way but could go no further, and dropped him gently to the ground where Mother gave him a reassuring lick. Then, with an unaccustomed strength of desperation, I heaved him once again into my arms and staggered to the

43

yard where I laid him on the straw in the warm sunshine, and took a good look at him.

He looked a fine specimen, but half dead. I felt his black ears, nose, and white chest; tested his heartbeat which felt surprisingly firm, and watched his rapid breathing which had a chesty edge to it. He needed food, that special first flow of milk that only Mother can provide. But he could neither stand nor suck. We had to milk her.

We haltered her, tied her up and with a bowl from the kitchen Dilly relived his golden days as a herdsman. She kicked him. He persisted. Show this man a wild buffalo and he would have a pint of milk out of it within the half-hour. Squirt by squirt, kick by kick, the cow gave us a cupful which we poured down the calf. She had no more to give when Dilly left for the auction. 'Bid for the thatching ladder,' I shouted as he left.

I was now on my own with a calf I was determined should not die. I knew it needed colostrum – the very early milk – from its mother, a couple of pints at least. I rang a farming neighbour only to be told that she'd thrown away six pints last week. The calf weakened by the minute. In desperation I scanned my books and found a recipe to be used in such circumstances – bottled milk, warm water, egg, castor and cod liver oil. I mixed them, dosed the limp little calf and was rewarded with an opening of the eyes and a slight raising of the head. The vet came and injected him with some protective medicine, and I then let him rest and be licked by his mother and waited for her udder to fill. Dilly got back from the sale, and reported that just as the bidding was getting brisk for the thatching ladder, the auctioneer trod on it and broke it.

Late that night the calf was no weaker. Every pint of warm – though ordinary – milk pushed him a step further along the road to the moment when he could stand up and suck. Meanwhile it was up to me. He lay on straw under the ruddy glow of a heat-lamp, and in the gloom at the other end of the building I could see the ghostly white outline of his mother, checking on me. Her udder, I noticed, was filling. I never anticipated that when I grasped hold of a cow's teats for the first time, so much would depend on it.

New Loves (And an Old Friend Goes)

I HAVE NEVER milked a cow before and all the written words on the subject make depressing reading for a novice. *The Standard Cyclopaedia of Modern Agriculture* (1924) states, 'No operation on the farm requires more knack and concentration of attention and nervous energy than the art of milking.' Believe me, there was no lack of nervous energy as, with plastic bucket in hand, I leant gingerly forward and grasped Sage's black teat hoping she was sufficiently distracted from my groping by the bucket of rolled oats I had placed before her. I grabbed hold. The teat was warm, silky, pliable. The wise old cow glanced round with a look in her eye that I took to mean, 'Don't start something you can't finish, boy!'

Cows have it in them to thwart any milker if they so wish. They have a let-down mechanism which, if triggered, allows the milk to follow. If they are not minded to switch on, no amount of pulling and tugging will produce the merest drop. So I pulled just to see what happened, and nothing did. I squeezed my thumb and first finger round the top of the teat and yanked it downwards. The agitated cow side-stepped in my direction and I slithered painfully backwards on to the ground. I bundled myself back on to the stool, grasped again, and she kicked. I managed four or five more pulls, but no milk. The closed sign had gone up on the udder.

Then, in what turned out to be an inspired move, I hauled the calf on to its wobbly legs and gently dragged it to where Mother was tethered. You could sense the old cow changing her mind. She became calm, almost dreamy; there was no more kicking, no shifting from one leg to the other. She licked the calf, licked the oats in the manger and then with the next lash of her vast tongue, spread them over the calf's little head. Meanwhile, sensing my luck had changed, I grasped again and nearly cried with joy when I was rewarded with the merest glob of creamy yellow milk in the bottom of the bucket. It was a meagre half teaspoonful and the vet said the calf needed a massive two pints, but it was a start.

This painfully slow extraction went on for three days. In between milkings, I studied the books and improved my technique from the crude grasping and pulling to a more ordered and gentle sequence of finger movements like a clarinet player practising scales. I was told that one should 'cup one's little finger like a duchess, and squeeze like a . . .' but annoyingly they could not remember the rest.

I developed the muscular hand-shake of a wrestler after two hours' daily finger movements. But the rewards were great as slowly the thick, globby, creamy colostrum, known as 'beestings', crept up the side of the bucket. I would pause half-way through milking and fill the bottle and feed the calf while the milk was still warm, then back to the udder for another finger-aching session. I read that the last flow of milk, known as the 'stroakings', was the richest.

Slowly the weak calf grew stronger. Each bottleful had the effect of petrol into a spluttering engine. On the second day he was strong enough to raise his head, by day four he could balance but not move from the spot.

Then, on day five, just as I was thinking I might get the mastery of this milking business, I decided the time was right for the calf to assume his natural role. I milked a pint and gave him half from the bottle. Then I hauled him to his feet, took him to his mother, squeezed the teat and squirted milk on to his lips. Then I plugged the teat into his mouth. Nothing happened. He stood like a bewildered child with an oversized gob-stopper. Then, with one joyful movement of his tongue, he sucked and swallowed. There has been no happier moment on this farm. For an entire week we fought for nothing but that little calf's survival and so, happier than I had been for some time, I went back to the house with milking bucket in hand. I made a cup of tea, poured a drop of the precious milk into it, and toasted his continued good health.

'I COULD GIVE YOU your cheque back right now. I could, honest,' said Farmer Phelps in a Gloucestershire accent as rich as that county's native cheese. 'I don't want to see her go, honest I don't.' This touching scene was enacted at the door to his cowshed as I reversed my trailer towards it, a wide-eyed red cow watching my every move.

'Get Mother to come and hold this gate,' he called to his son as he manhandled an iron hurdle to form a race down which the cow could run. But we did not need Mother. The red cow merely followed her inquisitive calves who had bravely led the way, and with a few footsteps she was up the ramp and in the trailer, sniffing the hay, counting her calves, and giving me the haughty look of a lady who wishes it to be known that she needs no help at all when it comes to climbing ramps.

'I don't like to see 'em go, that I don't,' said Farmer Phelps. The only thought that prevented him from bursting into tears was perhaps that not only was this fine cow returning to the land of her forebears – she is a Red Poll, a native breed of East Anglia – but she is to spend the rest of her days on a farm not much different from the one she has left.

Like ours, Phelps's farm is out of its time. He is a commercial farmer who depends on his dairy herd for a living; but his attitudes and his practices are closer to what we do here than on any other commercial farm I have visited. Minimal amounts of artificial fertilisers are used and stock is fed simply and traditionally on home-grown hay and cereals. That in itself is not all that rare; but what sets him apart is his unswerving devotion to the Red Poll cow, an old and officially rare breed that a less enlightened farmer would consider to be as obsolete as the steam engine. It is true that the mightier animals produced by massive continental beasts appear to be a more profitable bet; but over a pipe Mr Phelps passed on his wisdom. 'An old farmer told me that it's not how much milk yer 'ave in yer bucket, it's how much of it is owed to somebody else.' A big beast *will* make more beef, yet it might have cost more to put the flesh on him. 'Trouble with farmers', said Phelps, 'is that they follow fashion. No one worse than a farmer for that.'

But fashions change and some farmers are beginning to appreciate the virtues of the older native breeds which they have been happy to ditch over the last fifty years. It is good news for Red Poll cattle for they are a truly dual-purpose breed, able to provide rich milk in abundance and beef marbled lightly with flavour-giving fat: a sensible sort of beast from a more sensible age.

47

Phelps and I parted before emotion overcame us both and I pointed the cow, called Prudence, eastwards. I took her for a big-dipper ride along Cotswold lanes which she did not mind; but the succession of roundabouts known as Milton Keynes had her bellowing. She has vowed never to return there. After six hours we arrived home and she ambled down the ramp, sniffed the air, nosed her calves into the shed and took deep draughts of water.

But life is never going to be the same for Prudence. All her working days she has been a dairy cow, robbed of her calves after a week and put to work to produce milk for the ladies of Cheltenham to pour daintily into their tea. Prudence has worked for her daily bread, spent hours in the clanking milking parlour being sucked dry. She has not complained; it was her career.

But now, in mid-life, she must change. She must learn to be a full-time, stay-at-home mother. This could be quite a shock for a working woman suddenly to find that her cosy office-like routine of the milking parlour is replaced by the constant pestering of her young offspring demanding meals at all hours. Still, she can always turn to our white cow, Sage, for advice. Sage has made a career out of motherhood, has raised four strapping calves of her own, and knows precisely the moment when the loving has to stop and the butting with her shiny black nose has to begin.

With Sage's help, Prudence will learn all these tricks in time. But for the moment she looks a little bewildered. Her calves are fiercely nosing her udder demanding more, and those quiet contented days when she had endless hours to herself in which to do no more than chew her cud seem far behind. There is a look in her eye which tells me she rather regrets I had not seized back the cheque the moment it was offered.

T HIS WEEK I was forced to make a phone-call which could easily be open to misinterpretation, should any unscrupulous eavesdroppers be at work. I became suspicious after a Telecom engineer turned up at the farm claiming he wanted a pound of sausages. Who knows what bugging devices he may have planted while I buried my head deep in the freezer and excavated under the belly-pork slices to extract his pound of bangers? Anxious to avoid any scandal, I have decided to make a clean breast of it.

I am having trouble with two women in my life. One is a romantic sort, with a beguiling appearance whose tenderness touches the hearts of all who see her. People swoon at the mere blink of her downswept eyelashes; men lay down their cloaks for her in puddles. But, as I shall reveal, she is a cold bitch who has cunningly hidden her frosty heart.

The other lady, who has just come into my life, does not have that instant appeal of the first. But she has swept me off my feet. She is solid and reliable, and has a sympathetic look in her eye when I pour out my troubles.

They are a right pair of cows. The first is Sage, our British White; the other is Prudence, the Red Poll. She has a self-inflicted eating disorder and I am not certain what she is trying to achieve; maybe it is a cry for help, given that she is having to adjust from being a highly productive professional dairy cow to becoming a mere mother of two young calves. But, for whatever reason, Prudence refuses under any circumstances to eat a mangel-wurzel, and this is serious. I have tried disguising them with sweet molasses but, like a child who cares for custard but not bananas, she licks away the one and leaves the other. The Red Poll is an old and noble breed from an age when succulent mangels were staple winter fodder, but Prudence will not touch them: it is as if I had discovered a Frenchman who could not bear the taste of red wine, or a member of the Garrick Club who turned up his nose at Spotted Dick. I have tried leaving them whole so that when she is tired of playing football round the manger with them she might be tempted to take a bite. I have even sliced them into soldiers hoping they will not be spotted amid the oats but this cow will not be fooled. All suggestions on solving this problem will be welcome.

Which brings us to the other cow, Sage, and her romantic torments. It is now nearly four months since her calf was born and we should already be making plans for the next one. Up till now I have done this by the simplest and most effective way, which is to use a bull but, for complicated reasons, I cannot this time. So Sage is booked to get together with a test tube. The whole process is done by professionals from the local artificial insemination centre, but it is up to the farmer to spot the instant the cow comes on heat.

Well, I have been closely observing Sage for two months now and the only time I have seen any passion flicker across her face is when the morning bucket of oats arrives. She shares the yard with a couple of bullocks who might be expected to get a little fresh with her and so give me a clue; but she is an independent sort of cow who might well batter a young bullock with her handbag if he were to try any of that funny business. Hence my phone call to a neighbouring farmer, the contents of which I will now reveal. Some may be shocked by it.

Me: 'I haven't seen her coming on yet.' Him: 'Have yer seen 'er mountin' t'others?' I reply that I have not. He then asks, 'Have yer 'ad a good look at her Volvo?' Not understanding the question, I ask him to repeat it. 'Her Volvo. Have a look at it. When she's got a red Volvo she's a-comin' on.' There is a long pause while I work out that it is her private parts we are discussing and not her taste in motor cars. We quickly discuss slimy discharges, and wish each other goodnight. I hope that publication of this transcript will bring to a close any cruel and out-of-context speculation.

But that does not solve my problem of spotting Sage at her most romantic: had I wanted to spend my days staring at Volvos I would have joined the used-car business and not taken up farming. Perhaps the clue lies in the mangels. Could it be that they have aphrodisiac properties and wise old Prudence, keen to avoid further pestering calves, will not allow one past her lips? Perhaps I should try feeding them to Sage, in large quantities. If mangels prove to be the food of love I shall feed on. The sooner Sage and her Volvo get into top gear, the better.

T HIS NEW COW of ours, currently called Prudence, may well have to change her name if she is to carry on like this. Prudence is a solid, sensible name. At the moment she is more of a Cleopatra. If I describe the morning scene in the cow-shed, you will understand why.

Since my failed efforts to get this cow to eat mangel-wurzels (I know that once she has tasted their sweetness and crunched the crisp flesh between her teeth, she will be hooked), I have had many calls from owners of cows suggesting I sprinkle them with oats, slice them, even marinade them in treacle. This has now turned what is normally a fairly routine feeding exercise into *haute cuisine* as I chop and dice the mangels before stirring them deep into the feed-bucket, vainly hoping the cow will not notice. But it is all a waste of time. She has a tongue as precise as a surgeon's scalpel and will lick every last oat from her manger, leaving the sad lumps of mangel untouched.

I thought at first that she might be objecting to eating greens on principle. She may have heard of the vegetarian movement who shun the eating of meat. Why, she might argue, should the meat not shun the eating of vegetables? But that theory was soon disproved when I offered her some stalks of leafy green kale which she devoured with a frenzy. Of course, she can live a perfectly happy and healthy life without ever letting a mangel past her molars, but when I see the other cows getting such joy from grinding the succulent roots twice daily between their teeth, I feel sorry that she is missing out on a treat.

So every morning I tie her to the hay-rack and we go through a little routine. I ought to explain that although I bought her with two calves, it soon became clear that her massive udder was more than capable of feeding three, so last week I bought another calf for her to suckle. This, I admit, flies in the face of nature and Prudence knows it. No sooner does the little stranger latch on to the rubbery teat than foster-mother's back leg gives it a quick cuff behind the ear which sends it flying across the shed. Bravely it comes back for more and I help it by distracting Prudence, who, if she has something else on her mind, will happily let any numbers of calves hang on her udder. And so I tickle her under the chin, and chat.

Then I had an idea. During one of these tactile gossiping sessions I thought I might wait until she opened her jaws for a bite of hay, and quickly slip a slice of mangel into her mouth. I teased her with kale, which I knew she liked. Then I popped in the mangel. The jaws closed and crunched it. She gulped and it was gone. Every morning I stand there feeding her succulent morsels like a slave feeding peeled grapes to Cleopatra. Or, given the state of her udders, Mae West. After two days I tried mixing the mangels with her oats, but within five minutes she had sorted out the manger, eaten the oats and left the mangels. I shall play the slave-boy for two more days and then she can lump it.

But I shall miss our morning chats. This morning, for example, I told her about a fascinating document I had been sent tantalisingly titled 'CAP Reform in the Beef Sector'. It requires that each beef animal should have a personal passport. It is issued by the government, must travel with the animal and be produced on demand. I told her I thought it remarkable that just as Europe is managing, by and large, to dispense with human beings having to show passports at frontiers, the Ministry of Agriculture had managed to invent a scheme which requires cows to show theirs if they set as much as one hoof off the farm. But Prudence heard none of this. She had a faraway look in her eye and with the new-found freedom her passport would give her, she seemed to dream of balmy days on sun-drenched golden sands with tanned beach-bullocks tempting her with Martini cocktails, and not damned mangel-wurzels.

But her mood changed. A worried look came into her eye. Hey, she thought, I am no *beef* animal. I am not merely mobile steak on four legs. If the price of getting my passport is the certainty of the butcher's hook, I will have none of it. I calmed her down, and told her she had many calf-rearing years ahead of her. Sensing her vulnerability, I slid a chunk of mangel into her mouth. She spat it out viciously. This girl has spirit.

T HERE IS AN ANIMAL on this farm which has been here for the best part of eighteen months, but has yet to be mentioned. It is not that we are ashamed of her or wish to conceal her existence. It is simply that we have not been able to think of what to call her. She is a calf; a Red Poll heifer calf who is maturing well. We have high hopes of her blossoming into a good-looking cow. So far she has simply been the ''eifer' and so up till now we have said how well the 'eifer looks, or that is it time to move the 'eifer, or the 'eifer has escaped again. I freely admit that in moments of acute stress, I have even heard her referred to as the effing 'eifer.

But this must change, for we now have two other heifers on the farm and shall soon find ourselves in the ridiculous situation where I ask the boy to move the 'eifer, he asks which one, and as they are all as uniformly coloured as peas in a pod I shall have to describe them by their individual characteristics. For example, the smallest heifer has huge round eyes and velvety ears and could be well described as 'the one from the Disney film'. The other heifer is a little long in the leg and might be nicknamed 'Lanky'. But these things lie in the eye of the individual beholder, and would make for a confusing state of affairs.

I have been putting off the heifer's christening though, for these things are never quite as simple as they appear. In my ignorance I fondly imagined that I could simply turn to any *Child's Book of the Farm* written in the fifties and borrow names from that; we would then end up with Blossom, Buttercup, Daisy and Bluebell. But I had forgotten that our cattle are pure-born and pedigree and certain rules apply. To start with, each name must carry a prefix which is the name of the herd from which they come; for example, a cow called Ford Escort would come from the Ford herd and Escort would be her name. The usual prefix is the name of the farm or nearest village. But in our case neither name is uncommon, and both have been bagged by somebody else. I am having to start from scratch.

As any marketing man will tell you, name is everything these days. How could you advertise for sale a mighty bull called Titan, if you had chosen Dainty to be your prefix? Dainty Titan conjures up balletic images, but hardly ones likely to command a decent price among buyers in search of hefty animals. But it would be equally foolish to establish the Rambo herd and expect a poor cow to sell as a quiet milker while burdened with the name Rambo Blossom.

Looking through the *Herd Book* of 1933 for inspiration, I notice that things were even more complicated then. Not only did they have names and prefixes, they had tribal names as well. These were allocated to animals of the same descent, and the names are a delight. Here we find Handsome, Brisk, and Fill-Pail. My eye fell upon Cheerful as an appealing prefix, but anyone who knows this farm will soon realise that to name our cattle the Cheerful Herd would be stretching it a little. No, we must have a name with authority, history and a sense of dignity. It came to me in a flash.

In exchange for these weekly dispatches, the editor of this news-paper is kind enough to forward me the occasional guinea. So I have decided to name the entire herd after this newspaper. Why not? They are both of noble descent, one representing the backbone of British journalism, the other the backbone of traditional farming. It would be a salute to both of them. Moreover, when the grass is rich and their rumens are working overtime, the cows do their share of thundering, so there is another link.

But the 'eifer needs an individual name as well and we have decided on Empress. Em-Press, get it? We shall treat her with all respect due to an animal that bears the proud name Times Empress. *Noblesse oblige*, of course, and I expect her to undertake a full range of duties. I have mentioned to her that she may expect the occasional invitation to present *What the Papers Say* or judge the annual Press Awards. She may even, in time, be asked to serve on the Press Complaints Commission. On the other hand, if she gets above herself and starts misbehaving, I have warned her that she could easily end up doing duty on the staff canteen menu. But that's journalism for you.

Anyway, I am dropping a line to the editor telling him of my decision. Incidentally, Wednesday is the day I am suggesting he takes his turn at the mucking out.

N EWS REACHED ME this week that old Mr Palmer had died. He was ninety, or perhaps a hundred. No one seems very certain. His face gave no clues, for it had reached the age where time could have no further effect upon it. But it was his sharp and watery eye that sticks in my memory and the way he fixed me with it when I was taken to his farm a couple of years ago to buy the horse-drawn binder that had stood idle in his barn for forty years. 'What d' yer wan' a binder for?' he quizzed me.

Nervously I blurted, 'To cut my corn with horses.' 'You seem t' be goin' back'rds to me,' he replied, and I tried to explain to him that I believed that by going backwards we may well find a new way forwards. He fixed me long and hard with that eye, and I suspect he thought I was going senile.

But now he is dead, no longer to suffer the misery of living on a farm he had long since stopped enjoying. His talk was only of faraway places and fondly remembered visits to Clacton as a young man. I tried to tease from him farming memories, but we always came back to Clacton.

The news of his death came from an auctioneer who had been asked, presumably by a solicitor, to dispose of what assets Mr Palmer had. To the best of anyone's knowledge, he had no family. 'It's terrible,' said the man on the phone, 'things are going very fast. Get over there quick.' His concern was for the horse-drawn wag-gons which he thought might be of use to us on the farm. I was there first thing the next morning.

It is difficult to believe that anyone would rob an old man whose body is not yet cold, but it was clear that much had gone. Two fine old Fordson tractors from the 1930s, tools from his workshop; even the house had been turned over. Thankfully, the waggons were secure, since the barn in which they were standing was in a state of partial collapse and it would have taken a gang of builders to get them out. I wandered round the farm-yard, deep in rainwater and several decades of unswept fallen leaves. Being careful not to bring any of the tottering buildings down on my head, I opened door after door and wandered through a labyrinth of out-houses, stables, byres, feed stores and harness-rooms. Strangely, there was not a lot of atmosphere. I guessed the heart had gone out of this farm many years ago. It had not been farmed for twenty years.

I was examining an old bale of hay, noticing that although it appeared normal on the outside it was of such an age that the inside had turned to powder, when I heard the distant smashing of glass. Picking my way carefully over fallen rafters and tiles, I found my way through what was the stock-yard and is now so overgrown as to be classified as woodland. Just by the old kitchen door was a blazing bonfire and a skip into which were being thrown old bottles and jars, releasing noxious odours of engine oil, camphor, paraffin, cough-linctus and fly-killer. I asked what they had found. 'Just this old rubbish,' replied the lad and threw a dozen more jars into the skip. But I knew they were not rubbish. Mr Palmer was old but he had not lost his marbles, and at the time we were hauling the binder from the shed he still remembered the whereabouts of every spare part. His jars and bottles would not have been rubbish to him. On my own farm I, too, have jars, containing black, brown, golden and treacly liquids. Only I know which is harness-blacking to re-shine the collars where the horses have rubbed against their stalls, and which linseed oil to massage the wooden handles of the plough when they become roughened. When lads as yet unborn turn up to clear out my place, will they know that the black filth in a bottle at the back of the barn is Stockholm tar, which I smear on the driving belts of the threshing machine to give them extra grip?

I wandered into the kitchen, and stepped back a century. Here, only two miles from a major trunk road, lived a man who cooked on a coal fire, heated his water in a copper and baked bread in an oven fired by wood. There was no electricity, and the cold water poured out of a lead spout into a stone sink. Paraffin lamps lit the room.

'There was a lot of old paperwork upstairs,' offered the lad. My pulse quickened. 'Old bills, farming magazines, receipts going back to 1920. Quite a collection.' I asked if I might look at them. 'We've just put 'em on the bonfire,' said the lad, proud of the effectiveness of his tidying. I could have cried. So might old Mr Palmer. You see, hidden among the boring old farming papers must have been treasures: his holiday postcards from Clacton. I hope he is there now.

3
Keeping Crops on the Straight and Narrow

F ARMERS SPEND such a large proportion of their time confronting nature, waging war against her and often winning that it is at times tempting to think that we can play God. However, I have been trying to reproduce the miracle of the loaves and fishes and regret to report no blessed outcome.

In fact, there has been no blessed thing at all. Had my little plan succeeded, I would by now have had an acre of young, sprouting cabbages: instead I have a field of blossoming potatoes. I admit it is clever to plant cabbages and get spuds but that is mere magic: I needed to pull off a more divine sort of trick altogether.

I decided that winter cabbages would be a good crop for this little farm, for there is a healthy demand for organic cabbage in the shops during the winter. And even if my modest crop should not be worthy of the glitzy supermarket shelves I could always feed it to the sheep. There was no way I could lose, I thought.

In my innocence I assumed that farmers grew cabbages the way gardeners do, which is to plant the seed, thin them out when they have sprouted, and let them grow. I have spoken to old farmers round here who remember doing it just that way. But when I announced to some of my more modern neighbours that this was the way I planned to do it, they chortled. 'Pigeons 'll 'ave 'em,' or, 'Slugs 'll 'ave 'em.' I doubted it, and bravely ordered the seed. They warned that I should follow their example and buy ready-grown plants in modules with fertilisers and fungicides ready-wrapped around the roots, and plant them by machine. It did not appeal. Besides, I haven't got a machine.

I was advised that I needed sixty thousand seeds to sow one acre, and it may interest you to know that such a quantity cost me a mere thirty pounds, making the dozen or so you buy at a garden centre for a pound look pretty poor value. The problem, however, was not the price but the volume. Sixty thousand cabbage seeds is not a lot: it just about fills a smallish pudding basin. Those seeds were, in effect, my loaves and fishes to feed a multitude of furrows.

But I could see no way in which I could possibly make them last. Although our horse-drawn drill has gears and cogs to make the mechanism turn extremely slowly, even at its slowest we would have used up most of the seed in one short run.

I convened an emergency meeting of the old-timers. This paid off for one remembered the way his old father used to do it, and this we hoped was the solution. We mixed the seed with sand to increase its volume and reduce the number of seeds dropped into the ground at any given time. 'G'up,' we called triumphantly to the horses and quickly had our acre planted.

Two weeks later, it all went horribly wrong and I blame myself for placing so much faith in a pig's snout. If anyone was responsible for the failure of my little miracle, it was those pigs. The land I had chosen to grow the cabbages had been growing spuds last year, and after the potatoes were lifted I put the pigs to clear it, hoping those blunt, black, probing snouts would dig, delve and devour every tasty potato that we had missed.

Alas, they did not. For a few days after the cabbage seed had been sown, bright green leafy shoots burst through the soil with the vigour of launched rockets. They were last year's potatoes coming back to life. This was bad news, for by the time the tiny cabbage seeds were sprouting, the potato leaves would have formed a dense canopy, hiding the sunlight and making the cabbages think twice about being born into a dark world. I could not even hoe the potato tops because until the seeds sprouted I would not know where the rows of cabbages were, and the seeds would not sprout while the potato leaves were hiding the sun.

There was nothing left to do but say a prayer. However, we have already witnessed the resurrection of the potatoes. Another miracle would be too much to hope for. But a commercial idea is germinating. If a few cabbages do come up, we could have a Pick-Your-Own-Meat-and-Two-Veg Day. After collecting their small cabbage and a panful of potatoes, the punters can then try to catch a pig. They deserve no better, the idle swine.

T REES SEEM TO MANAGE it with little difficulty, so do children and giraffes; but how am I going to ensure that the wheat I have just planted grows vertically and not at some lazy angle? Any deviation from the upright would spell disaster: we need it long and tall, reaching for the sky.

Wheat growers do not usually concern themselves with geometric considerations such as uprightness. Yield is generally more important and if the wheat droops a bit, the combine can scoop it up. But my wheat is no mere foodstuff: I am going into the roofing materials business.

You may not be aware of this, but thatched roofs are not generally made out of straw these days. It is more likely to be reed, and imported reed at that. But tucked away in a column of our local newspaper recently was a report of a meeting of the local planning committee. It is now their declared intention to insist that when thatched cottages are reroofed, they should be thatched with the original materials. If your old roof was thatched with straw, you will not be allowed to rethatch it with reed. This is good news if you are a straw grower, as I intend to be.

The difference between a straw roof and one made of reed is the difference between a fluffy cushion and a hard-seated bench. Reed thatch is sharp and angular, appealing to those who like neatly shaped flower beds and lawns with razor-sharp edges. Long straw thatch, on the other hand, flops over a house like a fat down pillow, sheltering all beneath.

Needless to say, modern agriculture does not serve the thatcher well. He needs his straw to be long and durable, and it is no use to him when it has been through a combine-harvester. It emerges muddled, fragmented, and battered. What you need is an old-fashioned binder like ours, which ties the corn into neat sheaves without even bending the straw. You then feed those sheaves into the threshing machine (we've got one of those, too) which also treats the straw in a firm but gentle manner. This gives the thatcher his raw material, and the farmer a gratifying chance to sell his product twice, marketing both the grain and the stalk that held it.

But you need the right seed, and had it not been for a chance meeting with a thatcher, Mr Cousins, my project might never have got off the ground.

Mr Cousins (or Major Cousins as he styles himself in the telephone book: perhaps he simply commands his wheat to stand to attention and achieves the upright effect that way) is a walking encyclopedia of wheat. He has dried straws in his house which he waves and declares to be 'related to an old Russian spring wheat!' or to have been 'around since Egyptian times'. His enthusiasm is infectious. I had not thought of wheat-growing as anything more than putting seed into the ground and hoping for a harvest; but I now long to write across my fields one more chapter in a long and noble history.

Old-fashioned wheats have delightful names. He showed me Rampton Rivet and Little Joss. Where was Rampton, who was Joss? Then we came to a variety known as Squarehead's Master. Who was square-headed, and how did this wheat become master of him? Perhaps I am to find out.

We scooped a few hundredweight of this rare and precious grain into bags and I asked when it should be sown, to be told simply, 'Yesterday.' The horses were harnessed, the seed drill dragged from the shed and dusted down, and in rows as straight as I could possibly manage the seed was sown. I found it a moving experience, like attending the birth of the offspring of an endangered species. I vowed to give it loving care and attention.

Consequently the yellow and black fluttering bird-scaring kite which did us proud last year was uncovered from the back of the barn. It is now flying high and hawklike in the breeze, and the marauding rooks and crows, I hope, are knocking their knees in terror and resolving not even to point a felonious beak at my field of rare and precious wheat.

We sowed it a month ago and it has just sprouted. Some shoots are not quite as upright as I would like but I will allow them a wavering childhood. However, let the wheat be warned. Any sloppy behaviour, and I am sending for the Major.

Keeping Crops on the Straight and Narrow

L EST YOU SHOULD THINK that I am becoming in any way
a competent farmer, let me tell you a story that has been
brought to mind by the approach of the harvest season. To adapt
the old nursery rhyme, it is a song with, alas, no sixpence in it, but
an enormous pocketful of rye.

One of the very first crops that I grew when we came here was
rye. I was encouraged by my library of aged farming tomes from
whence cometh all my understanding of traditional farming. Of rye
they say, 'a rank growth so succulent . . . the earliest food for
sheep . . .' Of the grain they remark, 'On the Continent it forms
the principal article of food of the labouring classes.' It was clear
that rye is one of those hardy crops, thrifty in its ways and willing
to grow under farming conditions as barren as Blackpool beach. It
sounded exactly the copper-bottomed sort of crop a beginner ought
to grow.

Except that I didn't want a crop of mature rye. I wanted a field
of fresh, sprouting rye shoots on which to graze the stock. Rye is
a rapid grower and even by the middle of January when all other
growth has come to a freezing halt, it is safe to graze it lightly with
sheep without doing any permanent damage. It is also good for the
sheep to have some fresh green feed at a time when it is scarce; and
it is even better for the other meadows, for there is no temptation
to turn out the flock when the grass ought to be resting.

But what no book warned me about was the staying power of
this stuff. Rye clings to the earth like a drunk to a bar at closing
time. Sure enough, our October-sown crop flourished and by February the sheep were gobbling as much as they could handle. At one
stage we brought in an extra hundred sheep just to keep the
flourishing rye in check. Within a fortnight, the hundred hungry
ewes had grazed it bare till the shoots met the dust. I sent the
visiting flock home with thanks. Within a fortnight, and despite
cripplingly low temperatures, the rye was up and fighting again. I
rang the shepherd. The hundred ewes returned and poured out of
the lorry like a peckish old-folks'-outing drawing up at a Little
Chef. One week and it was all gone. The ewes went home.

Three weeks later the rye was back and sprouting even more

vigorously in the increasing warmth of the lengthening days. It had survived two massive attacks, and desperate measures were called for. We used spring-tine harrows, a vicious wide-toothed comb which ran backwards and forwards till every fleck of green had been removed from the landscape. I looked at the field when we had finished, thanked the rye for the valuable service it had provided in feeding the sheep through the winter, and apologised for putting such a brutal end to its life.

Within a week, it was back. Like an unwelcome relative waving from the approaching train, the slender green shoots were once again swaying depressingly in the early spring breezes. I called an end to the game, admitted defeat, and let the crop grow to maturity. We harvested it with the binder, grudgingly carted it to the stack, and reluctantly put it through the threshing machine to extract the grain.

But the worst was yet to come. I thought that at least for all my efforts I would now have several tonnes of rye for sale and could look forward to a profit on the whole tormenting exercise. But the few grain dealers we rang did not seem very interested. I told them that those Ryvita people must be crying out for it, but they were not swayed. In desperation I screamed, 'But what about the labouring classes on the Continent? Surely they would welcome it?'

Having persuaded no one of its value, we humped the bags on to a trailer and hid them in a dark recess of the barn. Throughout the last year the mice have gnawed holes in the hessian sacks and my hard-harvested grain has trickled out like the sands of time. I don't suppose anyone will give me any credit for reducing the grain mountain which we are all being urged to do. After all, there is no greater sacrifice a farmer can make than to grow his corn and then feed it to the mice.

I had given up hope and was considering a bonfire when a pig-farmer said he'd give me sixty quid for the lot. I did some sums and added the costs of producing it, the man-hours in cutting, carting and threshing. Lots of rye, very few sixpences.

AT LONG LAST the suspense is over, and we can put behind us the long weeks of dreary guesswork and nail-biting anticipation. Yes, Alice the Large Black sow has delivered us a fine litter of nine healthy piglets. In pig-breeding terms, this is a good working majority.

Of course, it is nothing like the landslide of a couple of litters ago when she had thirteen, but we are not complaining. Her latest labours were accomplished with dignity and composure – with the exception of the usual percussive symphony in which she signals that her hour has come by flinging her cast-iron feeding trough high into the air and letting it fall heavily on to the concrete. The resulting chime would have made Quasimodo jealous.

She accomplishes it with her powerful but finely tuned snout which is her principal instrument of government. She has such mastery of it that at one moment it has enough deadly force to raise chunks of three-inch concrete, and yet moments later an escaping piglet will feel its gentle nudge and be deflected back to the warmth and shelter of the sty. Autocratic, yet caring; that's our Alice.

Also this week, apart from the squealing litter of black piglets, a decidedly black-looking parcel arrived in the post which has caused me much excitement, and thrown my family into a deep gloom.

I mentioned some time ago that my unfulfilled ambition was to make porridge by rolling my own oats. It proved impossible for I could find no way of separating the luscious groats from the indigestible husks. In fact, I now know that I was wasting my time, for a company with the boastful name of *Superioats* wrote to say that what I should be growing were 'naked oats', so called because they have no husk. It would be a simple matter to roll them, carry them to the stove, and live happily ever after. They sent a sample to prove it and I confess I have never tasted better porridge.

Instead of writing a simple letter of thanks, I set them a further problem. Old horsemen have often mentioned to me that they used to grow a variety of oat called 'black oats'. 'Hell!' they would insist. 'Them black utz, them were good grub for 'osses.' Apparently, there was no finer feed for the working cart-horse than these plump, fattening, invigorating black grains. But where to find the seed? I asked various merchants but got no response. And when I wrote to Superioats, there was no immediate response. This dinosaur of a cereal, I guessed, had become extinct.

But last week, a parcel the size of a bag of sweets arrived in the post. Inside were a couple of pounds of precious black oat seed. I gazed into the bag like Howard Carter peering into the tomb of Tutankhamen, and shivered with delight. Where had they been found? Was I holding in my hand the very last few grains of black oats in the world? Alas no. 'They're quite common in France,' said the man from Superioats. 'They grow them for horses. None grown in this country, though.'

So I intend to correct that sorry state of affairs. My cart-horses expect no less of me. It will, of course, take years. I shall plant the few seeds that I have, harvest them and thresh them on the floor of the barn to remove the grain. I shall then sow those the following year, and so on till I have enough seed to plant a crop. It is fraught with danger. One hungry rabbit which happened to stumble across the budding stalks could easily wipe out the whole experiment.

The only thing to contend with now will be the black looks on the faces of my family when I break it to them that with so little black seed to start with, we shall have to sow each grain by hand. We shall scratch a shallow furrow in the earth with a stick and, in biblical fashion, drop seed after seed faithfully on to the earth. And then pray.

But I think it will be worth it because my *Farmers' Dictionary* of 1824 says of the black oat, '. . . very hardy, ripen early, adapted to profitable cultivation in some of the most tempestuous and least improved districts of Britain'. As I am coming to the conclusion that this is the most tempestuous and least improved farm in Britain, the black oats and I should get on fine.

I WRITE THIS principally for readers living in Middlesex. May I ask you what you think is so special about your hay-stacks? And if they are as good as reported, then you may be able to help me with a little difficulty I am having with mine.

My hay was made, carted and stacked in what I thought to be the proper manner; but after a fortnight of standing, what was once a half decent-looking stack has now turned into a droopy eyesore. When I carefully constructed it, it had classical geometrical precision; now it looks like a jelly that has had a traumatic birth.

And why might the residents of Middlesex be able to help? Well, when faced with farming tragedies I immediately turn to my library of aged tomes and in my *Farmers' Dictionary* of 1824 I read of hay-stacks:

> . . . the depositions of hay ought to be made with such a shaking action as will tear all lumps asunder, and render the whole texture open, layer after layer along the sides and the ends ought to be thoroughly bound in by the proper adjustment of the hay, and the whole exterior facing ought to be kept neat, tight and in perfectly regular form by the pulling of the projecting wisps and straws. There are no haystacks more neatly formed or better secured than those of *Middlesex*.

Clever dicks, these London folk.

Let me say first of all in my defence that when it comes to my depositions of hay, there is nothing wrong with them, nothing even a Middlesex man could complain about. I admit that not every forkful is placed with loving care but after the first couple of hundred stab, lift, turn, and flick movements of arm and fork, the novelty does wear a bit thin. All that is torn asunder is the upper arm muscle. You might assume that the actual forking of hay off a waggon on to a stack requires no skill at all; you may think it as simple an operation as shovelling sand but I warn you there are old boys lurking who will dart out of hedges and tell you otherwise. One such is Derek who is a regular visitor here and to watch him wield his pitch-fork is to see a man in command of an instrument so precise and delicate that an eye surgeon would be hard-pressed to measure up to his standard.

For a start, he does not simply dig his fork into the pile and hope that some of it sticks; he arranges it swiftly with a sideways flick to ensure that what he prongs is worth the effort. He then swings

his fork high using no more effort than is needed to give the hay
sufficient momentum to rise to the level of the stack. Even then he
is not done for as his fork falls to deposit its load, he gives it a
twist which flicks the hay over so it falls convexly on to the stack,
precisely into place. I dare say in Middlesex they do it standing on
one leg.

As Derek stood, looking at my stack and diplomatically choosing
his words to describe it, a thought came into his head which sent
shivers down my spine. 'That's 'eaten that's done that!' he declared.
'Eaten it?' I asked. 'What's been eating it?' 'No! 'Eatin'. You know,
gettin' 'ot.'

This was apparently a common problem with hay-stacks and
having had my memory jogged, I do recall reading lurid accounts
of the temperatures in the centre of stacks rising to the point where
they catch fire of their own accord. Derek remembered one. 'We
used to shove an iron rod into them stacks, pull it out and see how
hot it had got. I remember one that was so hot that when we pulled
the rod out and spat on the end, it sizzled. It was only a downpour
of rain that saved that stack from fire.'

This had me searching the farm for an iron rod long enough to
reach the centre of our stack. All I could find was a length of old
water pipe and I plunged this as deep as I could. It came out cold.

Even so, slight heating in places causing swelling or contracting
of the hay is enough to cause a settling stack to change its shape
no matter how carefully it is built. And so, preferring to accept this
explanation rather than shoulder the blame myself, we decided to
rectify matters by rebuilding the roof.

The impossibility of building a straight and even brick wall is
well known to the amateur. Imagine the trauma of constructing a
pitched roof where the building blocks are no more than bundles
of dried grass and not always of the same size. But Derek did it,
like the old pro that he is. And I now issue a challenge: if anyone
can show me a better hay-stack in the whole of Middlesex, I will
eat my hat.

Keeping Crops on the Straight and Narrow

THIS WEEK we have stamped, cursed, muttered, slammed doors, barked at children and kicked cats in a series of scenes which I bet has been repeated on every farm that still has corn to gather in. It is a measure of the depressing nature of this year's harvest that on a day when the seasons normally dictate that I should be tossing dry sheaves on to a waggon, instead I was picking up hefty branches of damp oak fallen in gale force winds, and clearing gullies so that a couple of inches of rainwater could find their way to the ditch. It is so long since we had regular downpours that I suspect the rain has forgotten how to flow once it hits the ground. It sits, bewildered, in puddles where none have appeared before. Had all this happened at the end of September we would have been delighted and happily pointed our ploughs at the softened, yielding ground; but two inches of rain in twenty-four hours with sheaves of corn still standing in the fields is a strain on any farmer's sense of humour.

But am I any worse off than my mechanised neighbours? I think not, for in my game the rules are easier. With knowledge culled from my collection of aged farming volumes, I took the binder to the corn when the wheat was 'still in a cheesy condition and the yellowness of the straw had extended to its entire length'. The book reassures me that 'final maturation, resulting in the flinty hard condition of the grain, will occur in the stook'. Modern farmers take a more scientific and less liberal approach. They measure the moisture with a sophisticated apparatus and until the needle drops to the magic 15 per cent, they will not take the harvest. In the recent wet and variable weather, it has been a common sight to see farmers muttering to each other like schoolboys behind a bike-shed, exchanging such intimacies as 'Mine's down to sixteen! How's yours?' 'Eighteen this morning,' comes the glum reply, and they all shake their heads with pity. Far easier just to say 'cheesy' (anything between Parmesan and Brie) and cut the stuff down regardless.

In my short farming career, this is the first tricky harvest I have had to face. For the last couple of years the hot sun has blazed upon the fields for weeks on end, and harvest required no more than straightforward effort. This year it needs cunning. I am beginning to see why farmers used to speak of 'winning' the harvest battle. My precious farming book of 1874 gives great prominence to the notion of a contest played out between farmer, corn and weather: '*winning is effectual when the weather is dry* . . . wind is also *winning* . . . to *win* the straw the bands [on the sheaves] may have to be loosened . . . corn *wins* in no way so quickly as when "gaitined".'

My eyes, searching hungrily for comfort, fell upon the word 'gaitined'. Alas, even the aged book describes it as an ancient method. It required each and every sheaf of corn to be separated from the others and be spread out at its base, like a bunch of flowers, to dry alone. It is comforting to think that there was an age when farmers could employ sufficient numbers of labourers to carry out such intensive tasks. It is all the lad and I can do to trudge up the field now and again and re-erect the sheaves that have fallen in the wind. So we wait for the weather, and in the great game of harvest, we seem to have arrived at a stalemate.

So I prepared the stack bottom. This is the strawed area where the corn-stack will eventually stand, and is designed to keep the sheaves in the bottom of the stack from coming to rest on the damp ground beneath. But even this apparently simple operation is fraught with indecision. How big should I build it? If it is too small, the stack will tower higher than is safe, and be vulnerable to high winds; set it out too large and I will end up with a squat little effort more like a slice of limp Yorkshire pudding than the correct 'loaf of bread' shape.

And so, even when the poor farmer thinks the contest is nearly over, defeat is ever close at hand. The rules of a traditional harvest demand that every operation, even unto the final one, be carried out to perfection. As I write there are still many rounds to go before we can declare a result. The sky darkens, the wind blows, the rain pours, the overworked moisture-meters have flattened their batteries. The sooner someone blows the final whistle, the happier we all shall be.

4

Well, It's a Point of View

S HARP-EYED READERS will have noticed a certain creeping Frenchness overwhelming this section of late; Radio 4 listeners have been alarmed to find it spreading even as far as *The Archers*, with the feckless Grundy family touring Burgundy at the behest of estate agents and government agencies anxious to attract young English farmers to till French soil. It is clearly far too late to spray against this Francophilia, so I too decided to sit back and enjoy its rioting blossoms with the rest. Over half-term this family abandoned sheep (and cattle and pigs) to sail across the Channel. For once, I exchanged my heavy boots and even heavier outlook on life for a lightly shod and jauntily natured visit to the western edges of Brittany, where even *les moutons* oblige diners by grazing the salt marshes and becoming, as the menus put it, pre-salted. We happen to have a field which has become infested with wild mint and I am wondering if I could achieve an equally natural flavouring effect by putting the lambs to graze on it. The pigs, after all, eat apples from October to Christmas.

I took a little light reading on my French excursion. I had unearthed in a second-hand bookshop a volume first published in France in 1904, which apparently took Paris by storm. It is *The Life of a Simple Man* by Émile Guillaumin and is the story of Étienne Bertin, otherwise known as Tiennon, a French countryman with whom Monsieur Guillaumin took up. It is not romantic. 'His world is one of unremitting toil; he is cheated by landlords and patronised by smart city people. In the fields there is a ceaseless battle against crop failures and the vagaries of the weather', it says on the back. The front bears a detail from a Van Gogh sketch of some poor bent-backed devil hoeing, just as I have been doing in the summer pursuit of 'choppin' 'aht mangels'. It is the time of year when the mangel-wurzel seeds germinate and in order to ensure fully grown mangels as big as cannon-balls they have to be thinned to about a foot apart. It is done with a hoe, backwards and forwards, all day long, row after row. It hurts. Smart city people look over the hedge in their green wellies and probably patronise me while I do it. This was clearly my sort of book.

Old Tiennon looked the part. 'A dear old fellow, all bent with age, unable to walk without the help of his hazel stick. He has a thin fringe of white beard, and a wart on the side of his nose . . . a big cotton smock with a leather belt, baggy blue trousers, a woollen cap turned down over his ears and sabots of beechwood bound with iron hoops.' He has certain endearing habits, like halting his oxen at the end of every furrow for a pinch of snuff (for him, not them) in winter, and in summer taking a further pinch between every swipe of his scythe. But his account of country life is unvarnished, not at all the stuff to charm passing ad-men into writing best-sellers. At six years old he tended sheep for long hours in the hot sun, dreading snakes. In adolescence he went courting, a fairly dour affair ('"As well you as another," she said'). In youth he watched his parents and grandmother dreading ruin at the landlord's hand ('"The lawyers will take our all. They will sell our furniture and our tools at auction. *Ah, mon Dieu!*"'). His family epitaph was 'He was very old, worn out, but he wasn't a burden. He worked right to the end.' In other words, it sounds just like farming life anywhere else.

Obviously this book will never be a best-seller. Having reluctantly accepted that our own rural dream is long since buried beneath fields of rape and out-of-town hypermarkets, we prefer our images of the French farming landscape to be incurably romantic. Our French farmer is still the one in the TV commercials: a casual man, amid chickens which cackle endearingly and ripe grapes which cascade from the vine. A man who can finish work in time for endless hours in the shade sipping rough red wine and dining simply off the fruits of the land, with his black-clad granny and Monsieur *le curé* alongside. His life, we suppose, is one long Furrow in Provence and we do not want to know about his backache. Or, to bring it up to date, his subsidy problems.

I put the book aside and tried to enjoy the holiday. I do not suppose the French farmer is at heart much different from the British, except that he is readier to take to the streets and barricades when he thinks his government has failed him. In the long run, I doubt he sees much future on the land. But he has given me a few ideas, has Tiennon. Does anybody know where I could buy snuff these days?

W HEN WE GET PHONE-CALLS trying to sell us double-glazing, we carefully explain that this backward little farm has hardly got to grips with single glazing yet. Coupled with a wild mooing in the background, this usually puts them off. However, my wife took another sort of call recently and her best efforts were hardly able to put the saleswoman off.

She was calling from a magazine with the title of *Big Farm Weekly*. As it is a mere forty-four pages long we must assume that the *Big* refers to the farm and not the size of the publication. This sets it apart, for I know of no other rag — not on the lower shelves anyway — which puts such emphasis on the size of its readers' assets. Have you ever heard of a gardening magazine called *Big Shrub Monthly*? Or a cookery magazine only for chefs who own cake-tins larger than ten inches? *Big Farm Weekly*, I fear, is written for the cow-pie eaters, the Desperate Dans of the farming world who think bigger is better because it produces more. Regular readers will know that this is not the principle on which this model farm is run.

And so the poor saleswoman found it an uphill struggle to per-suade herself that we qualified for the free subscription list. I believe you have to farm 400 acres or more to join this Big Boys club; we farm forty. On being told this, she grasped at straws. 'Stock numbers do count, of course,' she said. 'Well, there are pigs,' said my wife politely. The woman brightened, assuming we were an intensive pig unit. Forty acres of tin pig sheds would indeed be a giant, so the honour of a subscription could easily fall upon our shoulders. So: 'How many sows do you have?' 'Er — two.' 'Two hundred?' she asked in a hopeful sort of way. 'No, just the two. But Alice is ever so pregnant.'

Still she did not flinch. 'Oh, I see. So you must be a horticultural

unit, then.' She clearly could not believe there was a piece of farm-
land left which was not under intensive cultivation. 'How many
acres of brassicas?' 'Er, just the one,' my wife said hesitantly; the
last thing she wished to do was deceive. 'But – er – actually we
haven't strictly speaking got even that yet because a wooden bit
has fallen off the seed-drill and my husband means to make another
but he can't till he can sharpen his chisel and someone has borrowed
the block and . . .' In the end we waved the clove of garlic before
the devil and told her we were not only pathetically under-endowed,
but organic as well. She gave up.

So I do not expect to find *Big Farm Weekly* arriving in the post;
but it hardly matters because my neighbour gets it. I am looking
at a typical page where the first story on the subject of disease in
wheat says, 'Our advice would be to spray if the threshold of . . .'
The next story begins, 'Get a fungicide spray on to winter wheat
crops as soon as . . .' and at the bottom of the page comes news
that 'French sprayer maker Berthoud plans to unveil a new mounted
sprayer that . . .' I expect page three offers its readers Big Nozzles
of the Week.

However, the editorial worries me less than some of the advertise-
ments. In particular, the breeders of a new variety of oil-seed rape
have chosen to extol the virtues of their new seed by mocking what
they refer to as 'old wives' tales'. In a long piece of copy they
attempt to persuade us that we need no longer rely on the old
traditions as plant geneticists have rendered them redundant. For
example, they tell us that corn dolls were made from the straw of
the last sheaf gathered at harvest and were ceremoniously ploughed
into the first furrow at the next planting, thereby completing the
circle. This to the Big Farmer is heresy. Never let it be said that he
ever returns anything of goodness to the land: the other Big Boys
might call him a cissy. Completing a natural cycle by ploughing
back vegetation to build humus in the soil is the sort of thing they
go behind the tractor sheds to laugh about.

They also mock the hillside effigy of the Long Man of Cerne
Abbas, the ringing of bells to ward off thunder, and the Plough
Monday festival. But have they tested them? When they pour scorn

on the ancient wisdom that sowing seeds naked by the light of the full moon ensures a bumper harvest, how do they know it is not true? It seems wrong that such a scientifically engineered product should be promoted on the basis of rejecting other theories without testing. I challenge the makers of this seed to strip off at the next full moon and cast their seed before them, with a photographer from *Big Farm Weekly* in attendance. That should sort the Big Men from the Boys.

D EPRESSED, DISHEARTENED and shattered, I stumbled to the farm-yard clutching a copy of *The Times*. It contained the most fluent and comprehensive demolition of organic farming that I have read. I quote: 'The notion that organic equals natural equals good for you is superstitious mumbo-jumbo ... there is nothing wicked about "inorganic" synthetic nitrates or ammonium salts ...' There was much more. My organic foundations were rocked.

Clutching the newspaper, I strolled to the yard to talk it over, as we cranks do, with the plants. Actually, it was the pigs I spoke to first. I asked Alice, the Large Black sow, if she would like her litter routinely injected with iron as is the non-organic farming practice. She thanked me, but pointed out that pigs that root in the soil generally get all the minerals they need. I suggested a further round of injections, just in case some illness might strike. She did not fancy that either. She said that, leading a relaxed life and being fed cereals with no additives, she has personally reared over forty piglets and has yet to have one with even the slightest headache, thank you. She would rather I summoned the vet when something was wrong and not before.

I wandered to the meadow and addressed the lambs and ewes. 'I'm sorry, girls. Forget this superstitious mumbo-jumbo; it's back to the old intensive way now.' They realised that what this meant was an instant doubling, if not trebling, of the number of sheep to the acre. But sheep need their space, they bleated, and if they don't get it they get ill. No matter, I said, brandishing the newspaper. We can give you injections to deal with that. There will inevitably be a more rapid build-up of parasitic worms in the soil which you will ingest, but we have worming injections to solve that one. Except that increasing numbers of sheep have been over-wormed to the point where the worms are fighting back and refusing to die in the face of the chemical assault. It can't be fun to have the worm turning actually inside you.

Then I announced to the cows that things were going to change round here. This did not go down well either. They have developed something of a taste for our newly sown meadows which they might not wish to swop for a blander diet. I have seen dairy cows in fields not far from here make strenuous efforts to get their heads over fences in order to graze the verges, rather than eat the tedious rye-grass at their feet. In our meadows we have sown a dozen deep-rooting grasses and herbs to bring to the surface essential minerals. Of course, I could go to the feed merchant and get a mineral block and leave it beside the water tank for them to lick; but given the choice, I suspect they may prefer to nibble the cocksfoot, chicory, burnet and fescues. Would you prefer an astronaut protein-pill or dinner at the Ritz?

Then I did talk to the plants. I explained to the wheat and oats that to satisfy the egos of agricultural chemists I was going to squeeze more out of every plant. No matter that Europe has surplus grain pouring out its ears, we must produce more! More, do you hear? We shall slap on the fertilisers, and when this bloating diet brings on diseases, we shall fight them with more chemicals. Expensive ones, so next year we shall have to produce even more to pay for them.

I put the motion before the assembled farm-yard. Shall we please the man by casting off our 'sentimental and reactionary' ways? The horrified looks on the faces of the stock said no. They understand, as I do, that organic farming is not simply a question of spurning laboratory products, it is about animal welfare, cutting down on inputs of energy and petrochemicals, wasting not and wanting not. It is about creating a sustainable system to benefit a wider world than your own 500 acres. There is no such thing as a selfish organic farmer.

But maybe we need a new way of describing it. 'Organic' is overworked. In Lady Eve Balfour's seminal 1943 book, *The Living Soil*, the word hardly appears. She merely refers to intensive farming as '*no-return farming*': it steals from the soil without making any repayment. I have another book which calls for *Fertility Farming*, and another for *Ley Farming*. I put both words to the farm-yard committee for a vote. Turning back to the troughs, they muttered that they did not give a damn, as long as we got on with it.

W HILE FOLLOWING the aged seed drill as it deposited the mangel-wurzel seed into the crumbly soil, my mind drew a fanciful furrow. It occurred to me that my little farm is in many ways similar to *The Times*. We have our weightier chunks of clay land, as the newspaper has its areas of heavy thought and insight – and no doubt you have sweated a little as you have ploughed through some of them, just as the horses and I perspire on hitting an unyielding patch of soil. But across other fields we have thundered, making bold statements with our plough, leaving our mark for all to see and comment upon. This is our leader column.

We have quiet spots on the farm, too, away from the bustle and the bellowing. They are gentler grazing, not unlike the lighter corners of *The Times*. It is here that wild seeds have been sown, eccentric airborne fancies bordering the plain nourishing grass. Sometimes such seedlings flourish; often they are drowned by competing weeds, trodden on by unfeeling cows or have their tops unkindly swiped by the editorial hoe. And my farm even has spaces reserved for the humorists: the new litter of piglets is awash with merriment, like so many columnists, at having just discovered the joy of biting each other's ears. But even here we have moments of decorum: Alice the Large Black sow is a walking Court Circular.

And where does this modest column fit into the journalistic landscape? I guess we are the muck-heap. I know that muck-heaps have none of the stylish glamour of cornfields or the prestige of hay-stacks; but the muck-heap knows its value. Within its gently heaving mass, magical fertilising transformations take place. It is content just to sit there, knowing that the land will one day call upon its services for survival.

You may think I am overestimating the value of my Saturday column by drawing such a boastful analogy; but I now have solid reason to believe that this humble muck-heap is beginning to get up the nostrils of people that matter.

At the beginning of February, I warned that the Ministry of Agriculture may not be sufficiently well rehearsed at writing letters of condolence. Under the rules of a new sheep subsidy scheme, the shepherd is required to inform the Ministry of the death of each and every ewe in his flock, no matter how many repetitive letters this entails. I suggested that the ever-courteous Ministry might wish to reply to each and every letter in a suitable tone.

That seed was sown in the early spring, and I hardly expected a rapid germination. But a Mrs Bourne of Fordingbridge wrote to tell me that she had a ewe that sadly ate some of her garden clippings. True to the maxim that 'sheep have only one ambition in life, and that is to die', no sooner had the poisonous leaves fallen to the ground than her ewe took a swift suicidal opportunity. She informed the Ministry, as required by the law, and included a copy of my apparently influential column. The reply represents a major step forward for our caring society. A Sheep's Charter could not have achieved more. It reads:

> It was with much sadness that I received the news of the death of one of your ewes. Although the ewe was not personally known to me, I and my colleagues here extend our heartfelt condolences to you and the other members of your flock.
>
> I hope that the other ewe involved in the tragedy makes a full and speedy recovery and that the remaining sheep now eligible for subsidy survive their retention period.

The official Ministry paper was carefully edged in black. Miss Wall of the Guildford office, the author of that moving letter, may well be blushing. But she need not. Rather, it is my column which is flushed with pride at the breadth of its influence. I prefer to think that the dateline on the letter – 1 April – is pure coincidence. Proudly, now, the muck-heap shall smoulder on until the next time someone stabs it into life with yet another vital, forked issue.

Here in the hedgerows of journalism, we do our small bit. In the meantime, let others put on the heavy collars to turn the hard furrows of public affairs and shift the stiff clay soil of world politics. Gee hup, Levin! Git on there, Oakley! Hup, hup, hup!

I T IS HARDLY MY PLACE to offer advice to farmers on public relations; but just as our sow Alice cannot be deflected by mere fencing, neither will I maintain my silence on what I believe may be a solution to at least one of the farming community's many problems. The other night, watching a televised election report in which a candidate was attempting to inspire a meeting of local farmers, I could not drag my eyes away from the farmers them-selves. I have never seen such a downcast huddle of dejected men. They slumped on tubular chairs with the posture of half-full sacks of potatoes: heads drooped in resignation, legs sprawled, hands stuffed in pockets. There was as much spark in them as in a rained-on box of matches. Had the poor candidate announced free beer for all, few of those drooping eyelids would have flickered.

I felt desperately sorry for them. They were once champion heavy-weights who fought the land every inch of the way, and won. Now they are punch-drunk, knocked senseless by successive political 'whammies' as agricultural policies become as unpredictable as the weather. But they know all that: it is why they sit as they do, in defeat. What I have to offer is a cosmetic but bracing strategy with its roots in farming days long gone.

I had a postcard this week. It came in an envelope bearing a House of Commons seal, and it could well have been the most inspirational thing to emerge from the Palace of Westminster for months. It was a postcard of 'Old Shep' of Petworth, taken in the

1920s by the famous photographer George Garland. Now, it so happens that I own two books of Garland's work, and so inspired was I by this picture of Old Shep that I unearthed them. It immediately became crystal clear what it was that these heroic farmers had, and modern farmers no longer possess. One of the books summed it up in its title: *The Men with Laughter in their Hearts*.

To skim through these pictures is to see proud, upstanding men. Take Old Shep. His eyes have a wisdom that pierces the centuries; his screwed lips grasp his pipe of tobacco yet are clearly poised to deliver words of insight to any prepared to listen. Anything he said, you would be bound to believe. For all I know he may have been a miserable old sod who happened to take a good picture; but the moral for modern farmers is clear. If you want the world to love you, you are going to have to play the hero, and look like one too.

Old Shep is dressed in a shepherd's smock, but even I am not going to advocate that farmers start sewing squares of white linen together. But we could go back a few decades, before denim and nylon ruled the land. Also in my collection is a slim volume called *Land at War*. It is the official history of British farming from 1939 to 1945, when farmers really were super-heroes.

Standing boldly opposite the title page is a chap clenching two sheaves of oats in his muscular grasp. He is looking doggedly into the sun, his collarless shirt held by a stud, his corduroy trousers bravely held high by three-inch-wide braces. Over the page, the farmer leans on his five-bar-gate, pipe in mouth with a distant, wise look. This time he wears a trilby hat which shades his eyes. The cut of his waistcoat broadens his muscular shoulders. The caption reads '. . . with their love of the soil, their eye for animals, their capacity for hard work . . .' Wow! Those old copy-writers from the Ministry of Information could teach the Saatchi boys a thing or two. And if farmers could be seen that way again, who knows which image-conscious politicians might not scramble to be seen lining up alongside them, basking in reflected glory the way they do with heroic hostages, Children of Courage and TV comedians?

None of this revamping need be expensive. For my part, I have an old heavy blue overcoat, woollen, lined with silk and peppered with mouse holes. It drapes around me heroically. The buttons are gone but a bit of binder twine will serve as a belt. Such a frugal, manly detail is what the public wants to see. Braces seem to be an essential, so does the striped collarless shirt. The waistcoat, too, is vital, for it is a perfect match for the wide-brimmed hat. Farmers with a more humble opinion of themselves may prefer a flat cap. This will be fine; but remember, the wider the peak the greater the dignity. You don't want to end up looking like Mark Phillips, do you? Cast aside the denim and the sweatshirt. Take up the woollen and the corduroy. Grip that pipe in your teeth. The war for the sympathies of the nation is a tough one: if the other night's televised election report is anything to go by, defeat could come swiftly. Dress for Victory.

I MAY BE ADDING two and two and getting more than four, but I am now convinced that a couple of apparently unrelated phenomena are inextricably linked. On the one hand, I have noticed that the amount of manure that the horses drop after eating their hearty winter breakfasts has been on the increase. I could give you exact figures, so close have I become to the issue. It is, after all, very easy for them to do the dropping but it is I who have to follow every day with the shovel. When the shovelfuls start to mount, my lower back very quickly notices.

I had been unable to account for this laxative upheaval, having explored every possibility from soiled feedstuff to dirty manger; until one day I retuned the stable radio from the station offering current affairs to one playing music. Equine bowels instantly resumed a sweet repose; the daily shovelling diminished.

Of course, stockmen have always believed that a little music gives a boost to a lactating cow, but I had never heard of the reverse effect, especially in horses. And so I listened very carefully over several days to discover what it was that might be upsetting them.

I can arrive at only one conclusion: it is the forthcoming general election. I know there may be one or two Tories clinging to slender majorities who are suffering similar symptoms to my horses, but I must insist that for the peace of the farm-yard the election is soon over and done with. I am even having to keep the radio on minimum volume in case the cows should overhear and lose their contentment; to save us from a holocaust, I am fitting the pigs with ear-plugs.

On second thoughts, it may not be the election at all. It might just be the Budget. Farm-yard animals don't like budgets. They know that budgets invariably mean a sneaky bit less feed in the manger. When the farmer has been doing his sums, which he usually does round about this time of year, they know that the reserves of winter fodder are getting low and that corners may have to be cut to see them through till the fresh grass grows in the spring. That is why they are suspicious; for all of a sudden they will find that in a flash of generosity the farmer has dished out an extra forkful of hay. Only later, when the excitement has died down, do they realise they have been robbed of half a scoop of oats. If this sounds familiar, you will begin to understand why budgets make animals nervous.

I may decide to upstage Mr Lamont's efforts on Tuesday by announcing a budget of my own. As the stock are still in winter quarters, it would be quite easy for me to rise to my feet on Tuesday afternoon and announce what the next few months hold in store. Except that I cannot make up my mind. I have a slight inclination to court popularity in the hope of good behaviour in the coming months, so I have been eyeing my reserves with a view to organising a giveaway. Take the mangels, for instance: the heap is looking hardly smaller than when we started it just before Christmas, and since I can reckon on spring having safely arrived by 1 May, I think I shall announce a doubling of the mangel ration. That will have them cheering.

But there will be a price to pay. My precious stack of hay is fast dwindling and will be gone in a week. I have a reserve of meadow-hay but that will only last me through if we have no sudden turn in the weather when chilly stock might need extra feeding. So I shall be prudent and announce 'No Immediate Cut' in hay rations. They will like me for that.

But I am going to have to take a firm fiscal line with sugar-beet nuts. Quite frankly, I have fed them all and cannot afford more. Any reduction would be a highly unpopular move and would certainly lead to an unacceptable loading on my muck shovel. So I shall con them: I shall announce that we are becoming a more caring farm-yard in which responsible behaviour is rewarded with sugar-beet nuts. If the sheep refrain from barging through hurdles they will get their ration: if the bullock stops bullying the heifer, he too will be rewarded. As I know full well that none of them is capable of living in harmony and obedience for ten minutes, my ploy will work and I shall never have to pay up. I shall come out of my Budget acclaimed for being a caring and responsible farmer who showered them with mangels (of which I have plenty) and it will be weeks before they discover they have been robbed of their nuts (of which I have none). Eat your heart out, Norman Lamont.

N EVER IN THE brief history of the spanner has that vital tool seen busier times. I doubt there is a single farmer hereabouts who has not pulled out his double-ended friend and slackened the bolts on the plough to enable it to dig a little deeper. The reason is that cache of buried Roman treasure, unearthed by a fortunate metal-detecting enthusiast just beneath the surface of a field not far from here. I felt very optimistic, being at somewhat of an advantage over my neighbours: they are required to plough from the elevated seat of their tractors, while I trudge the furrows behind horses, and see more of the earth than they do.

But no luck so far. In fact, quite the reverse. I seem to add regularly to the earth's stock of buried goodies. On the near-side handle of the plough is a slot into which the vital spanner fits; but it was made for a wider spanner than the one I use, and so it does not take much of a bump to bounce it out of its home. As soon as it happens I call, 'Whooah,' to the horses but it takes a couple of yards for them to come to a halt. By then the spanner is ploughed under, and no turning of the furrows with my bare hands will unearth it. I hate to think how many tools I have lost that way. Probably in centuries to come archaeologists will mark down our farm as the site of an ancient spanner factory.

But I have been ploughing other furrows *this week*, and have unearthed another treasure. It was accidentally dropped by Mr Norman Lamont in his autumn '92 Budget statement, is worth millions and has gone almost entirely unreported. The jewel in question reads like this: 'An agri-environment programme was also agreed . . . £30 million . . . [to include] a new scheme to encourage organic farming.' Very few words, well hidden, but for those who believe in natural and sustainable farming it is better news than the entire treasure of the Roman Empire. At long last there is official recognition of a method of farming which has been more accustomed to having cold water poured on it by smug agrochemical barons and ignorant politicians alike. It must be thrilling for those who have campaigned for years, suffered ridicule and risked their livelihoods for the simple belief that organic farming is better farming. Now, at last, they find the good guys are on the winning side.

Even better to find that the members of the National Trust are leaning in the organic direction too. The Trust is the largest private landowner in the country (570,000 acres) and voted two-to-one recently to compensate their tenant farmers for any financial losses during the less productive period of conversion from intensive to organic farming. It seemed that the organic movement's dreams had overnight come true.

But this is where our ploughing hit a rough patch. For although the members of the Trust want their farms organic, the ruling council appears not to agree. They speak of 'No evidence' or 'Not possible for all farms'. These, of course, are now yesterday's ramblings: heritage arguments. Perhaps the trust should pop them on a tea-towel instead of trotting them out in real life. The organic movement has rolled forwards and left them standing.

But the National Trust is not the only body earning a niche in the organic hall of shame. Why do not the Royal Society for the Protection of Birds, the Council for the Protection of Rural England, English Nature and all the other nature-protection bodies not declare themselves to be in favour of organic farming? After all, it is the one single thing which would favour all their aims. A thousand acres taken out of chemically intensive growing and converted to an environmentally kinder method of farming has got to be better for the wildlife trying to live in it. More immediately effective, perhaps, than a nationwide mailshot inviting us to buy robin-emblazoned tea-towels which raise money to support officials who keep saying, 'There is no evidence . . .' There is. They should ask the robins.

Perhaps it is time for members of these influential bodies to do a little ploughing of their own. When they send in their Christmas orders for the box of Sissinghurst Soap or the Monogrammed Heritage Luggage Strap, they should attach a simple note – fixed to the cheque so they can't bin it – asking whether the organisation supports organic farming? And if not, why not? It is called throwing a spanner in the works.

T HERE WAS A TIME when a farmer's grasp of economics required him to know roughly how many beans made five. Ask him a similar question today and he might ask you exactly what you mean. Are you, for example, making allowances in the answer for fluctuations in the value of the mysterious green pound, and do you want him to consider the long-term impact of GATT which has called into question the entire future of the beans market? How many of the five beans have been set-aside?

Try another question. Ask a farmer how many cows he has on the farm; surely an easy question to answer. But according to the latest from the Ministry there are changes in the way cows are to be counted. 'The number of cows which are assumed to be used for milk production will be determined by dividing your milk quota by the national yield figure of 5,200 kg for 1993, rounded up to the nearest whole number.' How many cows make five? Pass the calculator, Mother.

This is not my idea of keeping financial control of a farm. Like our techniques, our economics are shrouded in the mists of tradition: this is why the farm stays poor, the bank-manager confused, but the farmer sane. Up till now I have gleaned all the principles of farm accounting from a slim booklet published in the late 1940s to educate young farmers. It is called *Farm Reckoning* and the front cover has a picture of an old boy, cap at a slant, chalking a few numbers on the side of the threshing machine. It asks reasonable questions such as 'A chaff-cutter with four blades is cutting chaff 1½ inches long. If the machine were run at the same speed but two alternate blades were removed, how long would the chaff be?' This is supposedly where the farmer slides his cap to one side, digs among the string in his pocket for a bit of chalk, and struggles to remember his times-tables. But would he? I think not. The answer, surely, is that the chaff would be too long for an 'ol' hoss' but 'that'd do damn well for them ol' cows'. QED.

But even my rudimentary farm accounting manual from the 1940s reads like an advanced text-book compared with a volume which has just come my way entitled *McDougall's Rural Arithmetics* published in 1914. It announced itself to be part of a 'series for the Upper Classes in Country Schools' and boasts a companion volume innocently called *Girls' Suggestive Arithmetics* – presumably majoring in vulgar fractions.

It advises us first to learn tables by heart. 'A sack of flour = 280 lbs. A sack of wool = 364 lbs. A bushel of flour = 56 lbs, a firkin of butter = 56 lbs, a truss of old hay = 56 lbs, a truss of new hay = 60 lbs.' Thus, with the knowledge firmly implanted that he who swaps a firkin of butter for a truss of old hay would have done better to have gone for the new stuff, we now move on to the chalk-on-the-wall questions such as 'Young cattle are fed on 63 lbs of cut mangel a day. How many stone do they eat in a week?'

But as any farmer will tell you, there is no such thing as a straight answer to even the most linear of questions. At least once a week I will ask a chap how much he wants for hay, straw, a calf, a couple of ewes. His answer will be either 'What do yer wan' give me?' or, 'That would have to best at least fifty quid, at least. If not more!' The true answers to farming questions cannot be arrived at by mathematics alone.

On page twelve we are asked, 'If it takes 2 hrs 35 min. to plough a ridge of a certain length with horses, how long will it take to plough a dozen such ridges?' The book seeks the answer '31 hrs'. But anyone who has ploughed with horses knows that half an hour must be added to every four, while the horses take a breath and the horseman has a fag. Then, at some stage, it is certain the harness will break, or a horse lose a shoe. It is futile to waste valuable brain cells on a mathematical approach to farming. Why should the farmer have to struggle to 'express 19.81 tons per acre of mangels in pounds'? He knows that twenty-odd ton is a damned good crop, about 35 tumbrils full and enough to see him through the winter.

Perhaps it is this dislike of straight answers which has infected the politicians who now run farming economics.

D O NOT BE SURPRISED if over the next few weeks farmers disappear entirely from the landscape. If you want to know where we all are, I can predict with some certainty that we will all be at our desks, swotting. Headmaster Gummer is setting us all an exam, and the word is that it is going to be very tough indeed: we have only to put one foot wrong and he is promising to cane us all.

This mammoth academic hurdle over which we must all leap is the *European Community's Integrated Administration and Control System*. Does not every word in that title make your throat narrow and your pulse quicken? A wise publisher once told me that the ideal title for a book was one in which every word took you one step nearer the till (as in *Country Diary of an Edwardian Lady*). Words like integrated, administration and control have you heading for the barn, rope in hand.

In order to comply with the scheme, farmers will have to fill in a form which has already been described as 'the mother of all forms'. We have till 15 May to work our way through the questions while Headmaster Gummer paces between our desks, flicking his cane to ensure our attention does not waver. I suppose the swots will hire agents to do the form-filling for them; we peasant farmers will have to do the best we can with our quill pens and hope we avoid blots. We have been warned that 'inaccurate application will cause loss of claim . . .'

Some farmers, faced with already complex Sheep and Beef premium forms, have used ADAS, a government agricultural advice agency, to help them. It is a bit like asking Daddy to help with your maths homework: he is clearly not to be trusted. At least one poor farmer in Cumbria is reported to have been given wrong advice and as a consequence is now several thousands of pounds down the drain. But it was not his fault and he is now appealing to the headmaster. I suspect he'll get caned, again.

But thoughts of all this were far from my mind last week when the sun shone, the grass started to grow and the skylarks were singing over the meadows. It felt like the Last Golden Days of the Holidays. Until, at about midday, a car came up the drive and suddenly the clouds gathered. The driver introduced himself as being from the Ministry of Agriculture. Ah, ah, I thought, the truant officer! What had I done? But he was a charming man, pleasant and courteous despite the futile task the headmaster had asked him to carry out.

He was the Suckler Cow Premium Inspector who had come to check the validity of our claim: a vital task given the ever-increasing size of EC farm fraud. He opened a folder bearing my name which had in it more sheets of paper than Vikram Seth used for his first novel. Then, in his best voice, as if at assembly, he began: 'I see you are claiming premium for . . .' and here he kept a straight face against all odds, '. . . for *one* cow.' I looked him in the eye, and nodded. The cow is Sage, our beloved British White. We have other cows, all Red Polls, but she was the only cow eligible and suckling at the time of the claim. 'May I inspect the *one* cow?' he intoned. We went to the stock-yard where all the cows were gathered, waiting respectfully. 'Can you point out to me the *one* cow?' he asked. 'Yes,' I said. 'It's quite easy. She's the white one.' Satisfied, he fled. Headmaster's little joke, I thought.

The next day a letter arrived and this time it was good news. I was told that the Environmentally Sensitive Area on which we border is to be extended and may well encompass our farm. Of all the schemes designed to protect and enhance the landscape, this is the best so far. It encourages 'traditional and low-input methods of farming' and offers grants for hedge-planting and renewal. Set-aside, on the other hand, pays handsomely to do nothing and the amounts of money now being handed out for no gain whatsoever are obscene. The sooner the whole of the nation is an ESA, the better.

Excited, I rang ADAS. I told them I had done my homework, read their letter, and was very interested in proudly winning their environmentally sensitive badge. But I detected some unease in the reply. 'Sorry. Must be some mistake. Letter must have been sent in error. Afraid you're still outside the area.' I put the phone down before he had the chance to tell me to run off and play. I wondered if I gave the captain a bite of my Mars Bar, he would let me be a linesman or something on his environmentally sensitive team.

That night in my dreams I heard approaching footsteps. It was the headmaster striding down the corridor. He now says that if we don't get full marks in his test, he will make us do it all again in Latin. *Quod erat Gummerandum.*

A COUPLE OF YEARS AGO, on a fine March day when the soft spring breezes were beginning to blow, I offered a farmer a load of what I thought to be spare mangel-wurzels. He did quite fancy them but, sensing he was dealing with a novice, he politely refused. 'Remember,' he said to me, 'April is the hungriest month.'

Until this year I did not have a clue what he meant. In my short farming career we have had a succession of mild winters and early springs. No sooner have the clocks gone forward than it has been time to liberate the horses and cattle from winter yards on to blossoming pastures. But not this year. The thermometer has refused to budge above the ten-degree mark and the clear skies have given us night-time frosts. It has meant that any blade of grass sensing warmth and rising to the occasion has received a sharp nocturnal rebuke, and returned to its slumbers till spring has truly arrived.

It is more of a problem for organic farmers than for conventional ones as chemicals can pull the wool very effectively over the eyes of growing plants. Nitrogen-fed grass is already tall and wafting in the breeze, having been fed to the point of having so much fat on it that it can keep out any cold. We organic chaps must wait for the soil to warm and the miraculous biological processes to take place before we have a field of grass fit for a cow to eat. So I agree: April *is* the hungriest month. Let it soon be over.

But just because April is the hungriest month outdoors, don't expect most farmers' tables to be anything but fully laden at the moment for there has been an amazing transformation in their fortunes. Only six months ago I stood next to a seed merchant at a farm auction. The sale of machinery was being held because the farmer had thrown in his hat and signed over his land to a huge farming conglomerate: another of the small boys had bitten the dust. 'These farm sales are like a cancer to me,' said the seed merchant. 'This is not only another bit of my business going, it's the end of rural life.'

The same man arrived on this farm a couple of days ago and with a beam across his face announced, 'Things haven't been so good in years. It's amazing. I've sold more expensive seed this week than I've sold for as many years as I can remember. Yes, things are really on the up.' A mere twenty weeks ago this same man was proclaiming farming life to be in terminal decline. Amazing what a devaluation can do to a farmer's pocket.

Of course, he's right. Despite expert predictions that farming was heading for a colossal slump, land becoming worthless, a glance at the columns of the farming press will reveal not so much green shoots as a rain-forest of recovery. For example, wheat for bread-making was £125 per tonne this time last year; it is now £170.

Cattle were making 110 pence per kilo twelve months ago, they now fetch 135. On top of this, farmers are now being paid *not* to grow crops on part of their land under the set-aside scheme. Imagine this translated into industrial terms: if factories suddenly found they were able to command prices 30 per cent higher, close down a section of their works and be paid to do so, do you think the CBI would celebrate the fact with a mere annual conference? More like a party in Hyde Park.

But I do not begrudge farmers their bonus. The small family farmer has had a difficult time and deserves a break. My main concern is what all this means for the farming countryside in which I live and work. I fear it is not good news. When prices were low, farmers could hardly be expected to find spare cash to help the beleaguered land. Anyway, with every penny counting, every square inch of land had to be farmed to the most intensive degree. Now that prices have rocketed nothing will change; suspicious farmers haunted by volatile European farming policies will now be desperate to cushion themselves from a feared collapse. Every square inch of land will be under a chemical blitz to ensure a bumper and highly profitable crop.

And still waiting patiently is the organic farmer, who knows he has many of the solutions. We would have created no grain sur-pluses, nor needed set-aside to control our production. There would have been no need for the RSPCA's new welfare code: ours is already stricter. But the pundits say organic farming cannot work (although, given the wayward nature of their recent predictions, that is quite cheering). Never mind. The Government is about to announce a financial aid scheme for organic farmers: pitifully small, but something. In the hungriest month, a crumb from the rich man's table.

5
Animals!
The Dramatic Truth

I N ONE MAD BURST of frenzied activity involving much moo-ing, plaintive bleating, and disgruntled grunting, the entire scene changed. It is as if a curtain has been rung down on the first act of a spectacular rural musical, and during a brief interval an army of stage-hands has moved the scenery and revolved the seasons from frost to cow-parsley in a moment. First on stage for Act II were the cows.

With the grass and clover well on its way to knee height, it seemed time to ring down the curtain on their winter season in the farm-yard and offer them a wider touring engagement. The cow and the bullock have had several seasons at pasture, but the calves were only born at the end of September and so they are new players at this grazing game. Show-business has always advised strongly against working with children and animals, and since the children in my particular extravaganza are animals as well, you see how daunted I feel.

So I called on the help of Farmer White and his team of lads to act as assistant stage managers and ensure the cattle tripped lightly in the right direction, and not down the lane heading for the main road.

I gave the cue by opening the gate. The cattle shot through like first-nighters diving for the reviews. They pranced along like a fat red ballet chorus, conducted by our waving hands and flailing sticks. Farmer White charges for his services by the hour, and I guessed that when we reached the meadow, such was their speed that the whole operation would have netted him about three pence. He would do well to learn the box-office trick of charging by the head and not by the length of the play. On arrival in the meadow, the confused beasts started to tune up with a relentless throaty moo. They seemed displeased, but unsure why.

Then it was the turn of the sheep to play the tragic scene, and with some justification. I had decided to wean the larger young lambs from their mothers. This is distressing for all concerned; not only do you leave behind a pitifully bleating lamb, you also have a cross ewe on your hands who has not only been deprived of her offspring but has been put on the worst grazing on the farm in order to dry off her supply of milk. She too bleats as if her world has come to an end. But you can never be certain whether it is the maternal separation or the lack of a good dinner that has caused most offence. The bad temper only seems to last a day and then life returns to normal; but it is a moving scene while it lasts.

Alice, the Large Black sow, only made a cameo appearance in this drama, having declined all major roles this year. She and her litter merely walked across the stage from the confines of the sty to the field of clover where she will hold her summer season. She wants to be alone.

But the least pleased on the entire farm is our matinée idol: our pure-bred Dorset ram. He is a muscular, well-endowed chap who in another life might have been a Schwarzenegger or a Stallone. Boy, has he got charisma! Of course, he'll tell you that he is but a humble bit-part player who 'just got lucky', but no one is fooled. The performance he gave at tupping time last August will be long remembered.

So you can imagine his distress when I singled out an old ewe from the flock and pointed her in his direction. This sheep is over thirteen years old and has produced twin lambs every season except this year, so we think she is probably past it. But we are fond of her and so she is going into retirement and will spend her final days providing company for the ram who might otherwise fall into the depths of gloom deprived of his bleating, swooning audience. He has to be kept away from the flock of breeding ewes, you understand, until August when we hope he will give another spirited rendering of the performance he has already made legendary.

But I can tell he is not happy. He feels that if he is going to be shut up with any starlet, it ought to be something more like Madonna than Mollie Sugden. It has to be said the old ewe does not have the box-office appeal she once did. Her fleece is rough, her teeth unappealing. The ram's bleat has a rough, offended edge to it. He 'simply can't go on'. But I have told him that the show *must* go on, because in farming it always does. It is a long-running drama and the intervals are too few, and too short.

I N THE INTERESTS of harmony on this farm let me now declare that I sympathise deeply with those poor souls in the public eye whose every move is made public and every emotion dissected in newsprint. It can be no fun to wake from your night's sleep fearful of each day's embarrassment.

I happen to know that this is the way the regal lady I have in mind feels, for although I have not discussed it with her directly – it is not the way these things are done – she has let her feelings be known. I refer to Alice, the Large Black sow; our first piece of livestock, the foundation of our farm and the figurehead of this little state. 'Quite frankly,' sources close to her tell me, 'she has had a bellyful of the press. She is pig sick of them!' She means me, of course. Her privacy has been intolerably intruded upon and she no longer feels able to settle her ample belly into a pleasantly cooling wallow of mud without some nosy-parker peering over the hedge and asking, 'Oooh. Is that Alice: the one that's always in the paper?' Things came to a head last week when one of these uninvited visitors produced a camera. In order to secure his exclusive shot he tantalisingly rattled a feed bucket lying by the sty. Awoken from a deep sleep she emerged looking far from her best: ears askew, eyes bleary, and tail hanging limply, only to find it was a false alarm. Shutters whirred. No doubt those pictures are fetching thousands from those salacious French magazines. Where will it all end? How can she be sure that the next time she goes to the boar the rat-pack will not be hiding behind the feed bin to capture her private moments?

I know she feels like this because in recent weeks Alice has been treating me with an increasing coolness. She had always been happy to use me as a way of channelling her views to a wider world, not being in a position to speak publicly herself. But last Christmas, when I allowed details of her farrowing to be made public as part of an advertisement on the London Underground, I found myself cut dead. She rejected all tickles behind the ear as I poured the swill into her bowl. Moreover, sources close to her have revealed that she is growing increasingly worried at the behaviour of the younger generation.

Phoebe, her daughter, is just back from the boar and will have her first litter this autumn. Alice fears greatly the publicity that will ensue, and wonders how the young girl will bear up under the strain. She is deeply disappointed that all pleas from her to me are met with an admittedly arrogant, 'Ah, but it is in the public interest.' Digging around in pigs' souls, she calls it.

And there the matter might have rested had not this great family been brought together by near tragedy. Phoebe arrived home last Friday and within hours of leaving the trailer suffered a physical collapse. Her back legs alarmingly ceased to work. She could drag herself along on her front elbows in the manner of a seal, but that was as much as she could manage. Rather than ring the vet, I rang another breeder who told me he had had a similar experience and was advised by his vet that there were only two solutions: one was an injection that would cure her but abort her piglets and the other was to shoot her. I didn't fancy either, and neither did my breeder friend whose solution was to turn his pig on to the meadow and see what happened. She eventually made a full recovery.

I sensed a world scoop here. I turned Phoebe into the long clover so that a casual snapper would not photograph her, and bided my time. By day six I was worried. She had not risen. She was not in any way dispirited or off her food. Indeed she was extremely chirpy, for a pig. But still she did not rise and I feared the worst.

Until, in a second-hand bookshop, I found yet another aged farming tome. It advised that pigs which fail to rise should be given brewer's yeast and cod liver oil. Off to Boots I rushed, and within the hour I had administered the dose. Ten minutes later – I swear it – the prostrate sow had risen on all four fat black legs, and walked. We all rejoiced. Alice forgave me all my transgressions and in return I vowed that when I put pen to paper in future I would be more careful. The family have been brought into line and decorum is restored to this little state. I know that Alice is once again a happy pig but when asked for her reaction, sources close to her would offer no comment.

I T IS ELEVEN O' CLOCK at night, I have just leaned out of the bedroom window and cannot believe my ears. This was supposed to be the night of broken sleep, interrupted by the fog-horn moo of a grieving calf. But there is no distress at all, just silence. The heifer calf, from whom I have today removed its mother, is taking it on the chin.

It could be that it is glad to see the back of its mum; everyone else on the farm is. From the earliest of our farming days this particular cow has been trouble. Whenever an escape plan was being hatched, she would be the principal architect; if the herd was due to be rounded up, she would be the one to plant obstinate ideas in the heads of the rest. Alas, the older she got the more cussed she became and so the last of our three original cows has now gone. She was the batty one, whose nervous wide eyes scanned the horizon like radar dishes. The merest hint of an approach from any of us had her poised like a coiled spring ready to bolt. Every farmer who has seen her has been of the same opinion and has reminded me that the 'butcher is the breeder's best friend'. Batty blood-lines should not be perpetuated.

It is a sad turn in my cattle-owning career but I must admit that I am partly to blame for an eagerly anticipated love-affair never having taken off. Much as I enjoy the sight of their vivid red hulks set against the distant meadows and their contemplative chewing of cud, I do not feel I know any more about cattle than when I first started keeping them three years ago. The trouble is that for large periods of the year a small herd can easily be put to the back of one's mind. I walk the meadows regularly in the summer, looking at them, but by and large they are self-tending. When they are wintered in the yards, so much time is taken up with the routine of feeding that little is left for anything else, like talking to them.

But this is all going to have to change, for despite cruel losses I intend to persevere. I took a short course in cattle handling recently and although packed with good advice, when it came to the practical it lacked the drama of real life. The first lesson was catching and haltering – exactly the skills I wanted to learn. Except that the demonstration herd belonged to the agricultural college. These college cows were haltered and caught on an hourly basis by student after student, so the whole exercise was about as difficult as getting a halter on a seaside donkey. They gave us a leaflet to take away called 'Cattle Handling by Rope'. It gloomily commences with the instructions for making a lasso. As it is my intention to create a traditional farm and not re-enact an episode of *Wagon Train*, I have set the booklet to one side for the moment.

I think I shall learn from experts, directly. My inadequacy at stock handling was finally brought home to me when the batty cow had to be loaded into the trailer bound for the butcher. He runs a collection service and his faithful driver Tom is to animals and ramps what Maradona was to footballs and goals. But it only works if you do exactly as he says, and if he does not think you are up to it he tells you to do nothing. At least, he tells *me* to do nothing.

He backed his trailer to the gate, took another gate off its hinges to make a race down which the cow could be driven, and then proceeded to round up the cow, its calf and a couple of bullocks which were in the same yard. 'Keep talking to them,' he urged me. I duly spoke. 'Get up the ramp, you old bitch,' I muttered. The animals were now winding up to a circular crescendo as they did lap after lap round the yard. 'The object is to try to stop them,' Tom offered drily, and I felt further diminished.

Then came his triumph. Instead of just the cow charging into the trailer, all four of them decided they wanted to go. He knew that once the cow had been in and got out again, there was no way she would return to captivity. He grabbed both of the slatted gates and with a quick movement of those two doors he performed a bouncing trick that would have done justice to the doorman at the Ritz ejecting a vagrant. And then he was gone, with the right cow, leaving me dazed. It was a spectacular performance made possible by years of bitter experience, and one to which I dare not even aspire.

In fact, so devastating was it that I suspect that is what is keeping the weaned calf quiet. Like me, she is dumbstruck.

I T MAY SEEM PREMATURE to be forecasting a gloomy New Year, but I fear that the strains of 'Auld Lang Syne' will hang nervously on my lips in 1993. We are like the toy industry here: thinking of Christmas while the summer sun scorches, planning things for Easter while Guy Fawkes smoulders on his bonfire. In hot July we sowed kale and turnips for the sheep in chilly February; while they eat it we shall be sowing wheat to harvest in the summer, twelve months hence. We hardly ever seem to live in the present and because the farmer's eye is always cast beyond the horizon, the days and weeks flash by and it becomes difficult to believe that the farming year is twelve whole months. It feels about nine.

And so it was on a hot and humid day last week that, thinking of winter lambs, I went to the field where the ram has been living a monastic life for the last ten months and penned him in the corner. There I bestowed upon him his chain of office in the shape of a harness that carries a crayon, brilliant red as a mayoral ruby, strapped between his front legs. It is noticeable that as soon as his eyes fall upon this apparatus – the raddle – he stands very still for it to be adjusted, like a king being crowned. He knows what is coming next. His summer of discontent is about to be made glorious autumn in the company of forty ewes.

We worked it all out carefully so that the first lambs will be born on New Year's Day. This is deliberate. I can usually survive the first six days of Christmas family jollity, but after that I find it very handy to have a flock of pregnant ewes to keep me out of doors for several hours a day. I can recommend livestock to anyone who is looking for a solid excuse to avoid relatives. I have often left strained family gatherings muttering, 'I'm afraid the old cow has a touch of the scours. I'd better have a look at her back end.' I find that if I make the complaint sound revolting enough, nobody will follow. Then I heroically and self-sacrificingly trudge across the farm-yard and have five minutes' peace under the hay-stack. Hence the New Year lambs.

But my little plan may have faltered, and that is why New Year may be a strained occasion. I went to see the flock the day after the ram had joined the ewes, in order to count the red crayon marks left by the ram on the ewes' rumps. There were several, but not the neat businesslike ticks he left last year. This time they had a distinct blur. The reason was clear as soon as I glanced at the old boy – he was limping like a codger with gout. This was serious. It was one of his back legs which, if you think about it, are more vital than his front ones when it comes to performing his duty. We caught him, treated him, and sent him back to work hoping that he would now have all the support he so desperately needs and that the crayon marks would not slither forlornly sideways any more.

Having sorted January, I decided to take the opportunity of ducking out of the pre-Christmas rush, too, by getting Alice in-pig again. Sows gestate for precisely three months, three weeks and three days so if she is served now she will require my undivided attention slap-bang in the middle of the Christmas shopping season.

I urgently rang round the local breeders to see who might have a Large Black boar. None being available, I decided to conduct an experiment I had been planning for some time. I am going to allow Alice a mixed marriage with a Large *White* boar. Logic dictates that such a match would provide grey pigs, but in fact they turn out spotty like Dalmatians. They also make, apparently, excellent bacon.

Now, it so happens that friends have a Large White boar, called Cyril. I asked if Cyril was free. Not only was he free, he was willing. So Cyril arrived by trailer to join the ram in the potent chorus now resounding around the farm. I asked, casually, how they came by him and they told me he had been given to them by a pig farmer who wanted rid of him. 'He had trouble with his back leg. They were going to put him down but it seemed a shame.' I froze. Two lame lovers is too much for one farmer. I am already very gloomy about Christmas.

However, the secret of good farming is to plan ahead. I hear from my wife that some rather distant long-lost cousins are thinking of staying – perhaps next July, she said. I have been to the calendar and counted the days. If I can just get the bull here by next week . . .

I WAS DRIVING down the lane towards the farm and spotted what looked like an isolated flurry of fresh white snow. As I approached it became clear that the snowy mass was on the move and heading in my direction.

It was no meteorological freak; a dozen lambs had decided that they were of sufficient age to leave their mother's side and had elected the lane as an adventure playground. The bottom rail of the yard gate is of exactly the right height for a lamb to wriggle its agile little body under it. They have it down to a fine art and can squirm their way through, hardly touching the wood; lambo-dancing I call it. I was hardly out of the car before they spotted me and fled as fast as a confused lamb can back to its mother's apron-strings. Some just dived for it, others were overcome by shock so brains did not connect with limbs: front legs were trying to sprint while hind feet were anchored to the mud. Never mind, I thought, heading for the workshop and a length of wire-netting, they will soon grow out of it and become as pudding-like as their mothers. It is just a phase they are going through: not quite tender little lambs, but not properly grown-up either.

So I take issue with a distinguished professorial study at an American university which was examining the sociological signifi-cance of adolescence in human beings and came to the conclusion that 'adolescence . . . has been a key ingredient in humanity's evol-utionary success . . . and it exists in *no other animal species*, not even apes'. I do not know which particular animals the good pro-fessor has been studying but if he would like to come and spend a day on this farm he will find it stuffed with animals all of which have turned adolescent behaviour into an art-form.

Take Alice's latest litter. For the first few weeks they were timid and coy. Enter the sty with the feed bucket and they will whimper at your approaching shadow and, for protection, form a piggy little pyramid in the corner. They are, without doubt, childish. Within a couple of months they will be well into their adulthood, spend most of the day asleep except at feeding times, and only take the occasional exercise by pottering around the field rooting for the odd worm. Nothing too strenuous.

But look at them now. They are bursting with life, developing strength they do not know what to do with, and when I open the door to feed them they come at me like the jets surrounding Officer Krupke in *West Side Story*. Their cheeky little snouts are into every crevice in the wall, nuzzling away at the mortar, pulling bricks away for pleasure. To fulfil their adolescent vandalistic ambitions I have even considered buying a second-hand bus-shelter for them to wreck, or a phone box to rip up.

Prince, our youngest cart-horse, is going through his in-between years too. Working cart-horses spend the first two years of their lives slowly growing up. At two they are gently broken to harness and then given no work for a further two years to allow their bone and muscles to develop. At four, they are re-schooled to remind them of the lessons of two years ago, and then put to work. They do not behave like unpredictable colts, but certainly not like a fully grown cart-horse either. Prince is definitely adolescent. We have recently been using him for some gentle work with the harrows and although he obeys commands, stands still when told and pulls as much as he is able, he has none of the placid dignity of his older workmates. Instead of standing like a rock, he throws his head in a juvenile way to see what is happening all around him. A mere 'G'up' will have him leaping into his collar with enthusiasm while his more ploddy partner has learnt to take his time.

And do not try to tell me that heifers do not display adolescent characteristics or I will ask you to spend an hour in the yard with one at that certain time of the month when the virgin young cow seeks a male companion and is unable to find one. In open fields, heifers will ruthlessly destroy hedges, fences and gates if they think there might be a bull on the other side. If they had underwear, they would undoubtedly start throwing it onstage when the bull appeared, like early Tom Jones fans. Cows with calves do not seem to bother so much; they have long since learned where all that lust leads.

However, I have to say that we have the answer to all this youthful behaviour, one any government might envy. Very soon the grass will grow again and the stock will leave the yard for the meadows. I shall put up the electric fences, turn the power to high and let the short, sharp shock curb any adolescent behaviour.

I HAVE COME to the conclusion that it is one of the great miracles of evolution that sheep have survived. As farm animals go the sheep is a real Trabant of a creature; reasonably reliable but never spectacular in performance, worth very little in part-exchange, in need of regular and tedious servicing, and prone to serious if not deadly breakdowns. There aren't any spares available either. But none of this is good reason to consider them to be dispensable, which I fear is the logical conclusion of the latest twist of government policy.

The trouble with sheep is that they break down too often. There are very few days when I do not have to take my metaphorical spanner to some old ewe that I find lying on the hard shoulder; every time it is the same exasperating problem. Many breeds of sheep common in lowland Britain, ours included, have an inbuilt design fault which means that should they ever happen to roll on to their backs, they are unable to right themselves again. It is like the old woman who sinks too low in an easy chair and has insufficient pull in her legs to get to her feet again without a helping hand. The ewes just lie there, legs in air, with a pained, confused look on their faces. They will occasionally thrash around trying to right themselves but soon give up and drift into that typical ovine state of mind which welcomes death with open arms. Remember, it has been often said that sheep have only one ambition in life, and that is to die.

And so I cruise the fields looking for breakdowns, and with my foot I gently give the ewes a roll in the right direction. I used to grab a leg and pull them upright but I have found that more often than not they have become so besotted with suicidal intent that they will fight me off if I try to help. Of course, once they are upright there is still plenty of scope for them to defeat the shepherd's good intentions. Having lain on their backs for what could have been several hours – I have not yet resorted to total vigilance and camped out with them – their rumens have filled with gases from the fermenting grass, so the animal ends up the size of a barrage balloon. I have yet to right one and find it floats away, but it is not beyond the bounds of belief. When these gases are eventually vented there is no mistaking it. Take all the raspberries ever printed in *Viz*, add them together and you will get an idea of the full force of it. But sometimes the blast is not forthcoming and I stand there like an anxious father waiting for his offspring to finish on the potty. What then?

Well, I have a little recipe. You take one cup of cooking oil and administer by mouth. The effect is quick and dramatic and for safety you should retire a safe distance since from both ends of the sheep comes a deafening report which would do justice to the testing department of a whoopee cushion factory. I am glad to say that I have only had to administer this medicine once. Having caught the ewe, I asked my wife to run to the kitchen for oil. Alas, she poured from the wrong bottle (she gets a bit distraught over sheep, I think she identifies too much) and so instead of a dose of Mazola the ewe got a mouthful of Virgin Olive in which we had been soaking garlic. If you have ever stood next to the extractor fan of a rather poor Spanish restaurant, you will get the idea.

But prevention is better than cure, and in a few weeks it will be shearing time and the problem will be solved. It is only the weight of wool on the sheep's backs that provides them with a tempting, and entrapping, cushion when they roll over.

I read this week, though, that for hard-pressed sheep farmers, shearing may be a thing of the past. With the price of wool set to fall due to the Government's having decided to withdraw price support, the costs of shearing a sheep will be more than the fleece is worth. Shepherds concerned for the health and welfare of their flocks will no doubt continue to shear for as long as they can afford to do so but undoubtedly some will either choose, or be forced, to let nature take its course and let the sheep, like the horse and the cow, lose their winter coats naturally. A sheep with a moulting fleece is a desperately sorry and untidy sight. If it happens to be standing next to a rank, overgrown and weed-ridden set-aside field, what a cameo of the folly of current farming policies it would provide.

I shall continue my daily round of humping and hauling sheep to their feet, and so will most farmers. But for the flocks of those who cannot be bothered, once again it is the animals who will bear the brunt of the new policy, and have to take it lying down.

AFTER SUCH A PASSIONATE outburst on the design deficiencies of sheep, I have spent time trying to think of them more kindly and look beyond their flaws in order to marvel at their creation. It has not been easy.

In these remaining few weeks before shearing, sheep are so vulnerable to attack by every other creature that it is a wonder each and every one of them is not on life-support. I have strolled round the meadows twice a day righting inverted and stranded ewes and have tried with all my might not to shout, scold or show any sign of thinking any the less of them for behaving so suicidally. I have gazed fondly on plump lambs nuzzling their mothers' udders; I have viewed them from a distance with a poet's eye as the snowy white flock drifts across the landscape like wisps of cloud. But still my sheep get me in a filthy temper, and something must be done.

This latest wave of disaffection has been brought about by a change in the weather. We have suffered from weeks of chilly easterly winds bringing cool air off the sea. It has hindered the growth of the corn and set back the grass; but it does have the advantage of keeping the flies in their winter quarters. The cows have hardly had to swish a tail this season, neither have the horses. But more importantly the sheep's deadliest enemy, the blow-fly, has not yet started his murderous little visits to our flock.

I do not want to turn you pale with the gruesome details of what blow-flies do to sheep, but in outline the fly lays eggs in the sheep's fleece which hatch into maggots which go immediately in search of lunch, by eating the sheep alive. The most miserable job of the entire farming year is treating a sheep that has been 'struck' but mercifully it is rare because we are vigilant. But even so, a sheep can be fine at noon and struck to the point of immobility by six that evening. It is that swift.

Now, if the sheep had been better designed this would not happen; for the fly likes nothing better in which to lay its eggs than the filthy rear-end of a ewe. (If this is getting a bit disgusting for you, imagine I am David Attenborough in his best hushed, academic voice.) But the rear end of the sheep is only filthy because nature allows an abundance of wool to grow round it. If there were no woolly bottom, there would be no problem. Of course, I can put the sheep through a poisonous and stressful dip but it is hardly economical for a small flock. There are also other chemical treatments, which are expensive. And so I deal with the problem effectively and traditionally, by dagging.

I take a pair of hand-shears (which must be stamped 'Made in Sheffield' or they will not be man enough to cut a piece of string, let alone the matted rumps I have to deal with) and I hack away till every bottom would do justice to a baby powder advert. It is revolting at times, I admit. My wife brought me a cup of tea halfway through one difficult case and as I reached for the chocolate biscuit, it was difficult to detect where my fingers ended and Cadbury's began. She withdrew the plate, markedly. You can see why the sheep and I are not the best of friends at the moment.

But I have an idea which may help me bridge the differences that divide us. The whole filthy business of sheep-dagging needs to be culturally elevated and praised in rhyme and song. The famous ditty 'We are all jolly fellows who follow the plough' has turned into a hymn of praise for what in reality is an exhausting, repetitive process of turning the land. Sheep-shearing already has its culture. I have a copy of a Sussex song which goes,

> Our shepherds rejoice in their fine heavy fleece,
> And frisky young lambs with their flocks do increase;
>> Each lad takes his lass
>> All on the green grass
> Where the pink and the lily and the daffydowndilly . . .

It goes on, and on. But what composer could do for dagging what that did for shearing? How can one make a moving ballad out of a situation where each lad would have to scrub his hands for half an hour before any lass would let him anywhere near her daffydowndilly? If Sir Andrew Lloyd-Webber wishes to have a go, he is welcome.

N O S O O N E R had the news come through than I felt that I had to dash round the farm spreading the good tidings. I scampered across the dewy meadows to the highest point on the farm and, like Moses on Mount Sinai, proclaimed in my deepest and loudest voice, 'Great news, everybody. The recession is over! It's Official.' My words echoed as far as the next parish but, alas, the livestock on this farm were hardly moved. I shouted it again to make sure they had heard. 'Hey, everybody! The good times are coming.' There was no response. I could see, written across their faces, that they had far more important matters on their mind.

Alice, the fecund Large Black sow, who has been served under two prime ministers, hardly felt it worth rising to her feet. Anyway, I suspect that going through her mind is the thought that more money in people's pockets means more to spend on the good things in life, and that inevitably leads to a longer queue at the farm shop for our special bacon. She looks at herself and sees inflationary times ahead. But I cannot blame her for being distracted, following the visit from her old beau Cyril the Large White boar who arrived with a view to producing another litter of Dalmatian-like piglets in

August. Since he was last here he has grown even larger, and if he and Alice attempt the door of the sty at the same time, we will have the nearest this farm ever gets to gridlock. They sleep side by side looking for all the world like a sack of nutty slack and Bernard Manning in fond embrace.

Unable to make any impression on the pigs, I took the news to the cart-horses who have now been liberated from their winter quarters and are enjoying the freedom of the meadows. Except that they are not taking as much pleasure in it as they should, for the grass has been very slow to grow this year; we have had too many chilly nights and need a shower of warm rain. 'The recession's over, boys. Do you hear?' They hardly batted an eyelid or twitched an ear, but looked sadly at the stunted sward as if to say, 'No, thank you. We'll just settle for a few more green shoots.'

I moved on to the cattle, leaned over the gate and waited till they were all assembled: Sage, Prudence, Bilberry, Ronnie, Basil and Times Empress. I lowered my voice a tone. 'I have some very important news for you all.' Sage bowed her head. 'The recession has peacefully passed away. The good times are coming.' Joy instantly spread through the herd. I could tell that because no sooner had the words left my lips than Empress, the heifer, jumped a foot in the air, nuzzled Prudence and then with one bound playfully leaped on to her in order to share the tidings of great joy. Thankful that my message had at least been well received by someone, I turned and started for home.

I had gone only a few paces when a worrying thought crossed my mind. I turned to look back at the cows and, sure enough, that heifer was still playfully mounting Prudence, who was not minding in the least. I guessed what was going on and it was certainly nothing to do with the news I had brought. 'Pru-dence!' I shouted, giving her name the full French inflection as has become my habit since unwillingly watching an episode of *A Year in Prov-ence*. 'You bitch. You are not in calf after all!' I should explain that, twenty-one days ago, Pru-dence was artificially inseminated and if she had 'taken' she would not now be showing playful signs of coming on heat. You might think that AI is one of those modern farming practices which I shun; but I have decided that a quick visit from a man with a rubber glove and a test-tube is better for the cow than a hundred-mile trip in a lorry with her calves, even if there is a hunky bull at the end of it.

We drove the cows back into the yard and phoned the AI man again. Dutifully he arrived and once again carried out his fertile little task. We must now watch the cow carefully to see that she shows no amorous symptoms in another twenty-one days' time, otherwise the man will be back to exercise his rubbered arm and if this should continue I foresee him publishing a memoir: *A Year in Prudence.*

With the excitement over and the cows back on the meadow I am now carefully watching Sage, the British White, for she, too, has fallen for the AI man's charms. But she has that deceptive look in her eye which tells me that she may be up to one of her tricks and be due for a passionate outburst of her own in a couple of weeks' time. She is a tease.

Meanwhile, over in the orchard, Alice and Cyril are making the most of their arranged marriage. Where only a couple of days ago I heard grunts of discontent, I am beginning to hear squeals of delight. Very loud and not unembarrassing ones. Love is in the air. Good times are just around the corner.

I AM TAKEN TO TASK by Mrs Ingham of Cambridge who writes to tell me that I have let her down. 'You introduce us to your beautiful animals to whom we become attached,' she writes. 'Could we please have a little updating news some time?'

The answer is no. In fact, in the light of recent behaviour by many of our farm animals I can hardly bring myself to speak of them. In every nook and cranny of this farm-yard there is a creature which, if not hanging its head in shame, should be. Except Alice. She has every reason to be proud of her latest litter; but for some reason she clearly wishes they were nothing to do with her. Every time a stranger approaches she runs to the back of the sty to distance herself from them and give the impression that they might just be some other sow's litter. I blame Cyril. Cyril, unlike her previous beaux, was not a Large Black. In fact, he could not have been more different – he was a Large White. Alice did not say anything at the time and gamely shared the orchard with her flabby pink lover; but since the fruits of their passion came forth, she has come as near to blushing as a black pig can. *Well she might.* Her piglets are the most extraordinary creatures I have ever seen. I considered what such a mixed marriage might spawn and thought we might end up with spotty piglets, like Dalmatians. These have the markings of pink pigs dipped in ink. But there is no regular pattern to them. Some are pink all over, except for a black bottom. Others are smoky grey, except for a bright pink ear. One looks like the map of Europe. But it is the shape of their ears which causes me most concern, for I fear they take after their father and have been blessed with upright, pointed ears. Alice's ears, of course, are long and floppy.

This puts me at a great disadvantage, for the secret of my success up to now in pig husbandry is entirely due to their ears covering their eyes. They have not been able to see me coming. This makes feeding easier, for they do not mob me, and catching them is less of a race for I can grab them by the back leg while their sense of smell is still working out where I am. Troubled times lie ahead.

As for Sage, her shame is now there for all to see. Having failed to spot the moment when she came on heat, I am now getting desperate. I must get her in calf before the time comes for her to leave the yard and go out to grass for the summer. So I have painted her. I took a thick brush and daubed her rear-end with a product delightfully called 'Tell-Tail'. Were it available for human use, I have no doubt it would be used in evidence in nearly every divorce case. Nothing betrays a passionate interlude like this stuff. It is applied thickly along the cow's back. When she 'comes a' bullin'', as they say round here, the other cattle will mount her, the paint rubs off, and the farmer sends for the bull or the AI man! But I suspect Sage does not like being daubed with bright blue streaks and, being a clever beast, I would not put it past her to have sent the bullock out to buy another tin of the stuff so she could touch up the original paintwork and conceal her amorous moods from me.

If this were not enough, we have recently lived through a night of violence. The two rams, suffering, no doubt, from a lack of female company since they were taken from the ewes in mid-September, fought and drew blood. Rams charge each other with their heads down, butting and growling. I hardly dare to advise the police on dealing with violent delinquents but they might like to know that I find throwing mangel-wurzels at the unruly elements brings them to their senses.

This brings us to the most serious incident which involves Phoebe, the young sow. I can only describe it as mindless vandalism. I blame her parents; or at least I would if Alice, her mother, were not being so coy about her blemished litter. Phoebe decided to spend the entire night flexing her energetic snout on the brick wall of the sty. Pigs have noses of enormous power. I have seen them toss troughs into the air which I have found difficult to lift. Phoebe loosened one brick, then another. Brick after brick cascaded on to the ground. Had Joshua not been available, Phoebe could have seen off the walls of Jericho with no trouble.

So I have that mess to clear up, the rams' wounds to tend, the cow's painted rear to inspect and an embarrassed sow to counsel. If you wonder, Mrs Ingham, why I do not write of them more often, you have your answer. When I write about seed potatoes, I have at least some illusion of control.

6

Rats Fight Back Too

A CORN-STACK should be a silent thing. Perhaps it could be allowed the occasional rustle as the breeze lifts a straw, or even a crackle as the sparrows dive-bomb it in search of grains of food. However, it is no place for a symphony orchestra to be squeakily tuning up, but such is the cacophony that I am forced to the conclusion that our corn-stack has squatters. I have only to pass by and they shriek like throttled sopranos and scuttle like thieves on the run. The whole stack is alive. We have rats and I know not what to do.

Were I planning an apartment in which a rat could take a winter holiday I would be hard pressed to come up with anything better. Our stack of wheat is dry, loaded with plump grains, enjoys extensive views over farm buildings crammed with sacks, straw, hay and all the other things rats like. It even boasts a Riviera position being near the ditch where they can promenade up to their horrid little knees in noxious mud and ditch-water.

They are a major pest. They steal the corn, fill the stacks with their vile droppings and plunder the rest of the farm, stealing eggs from the chickens, oats from the sheep and even gnawing through electricity cables to remind me that *they* are in charge.

Rat poison might be the obvious solution. I hear of one that comes in packets which the rat hauls back to his nest. There, he opens his little food parcel and offers it round. This kills all the rats in the nest. But I am reluctant to take the chemical option because of our visiting barn owl who now makes a low nightly sweep along our ditches and hedges and spends a good half-hour on the rafters of the barn, hunting. He arrives just after dusk at about the time I am fumbling in the dark (rats ate through the lighting wires) for hay for the horses. I sense his presence and when I look upwards he is there, staring at me. This brief encounter lasts for only a few seconds, for he soon takes fright and, with the gentlest hushing of his wings, sweeps the length of the roof and is through the door heading for home in a rotten tree. I have no wish to shorten his dignified and thoughtful life by offering him poisoned carcasses.

Nor do I wish any ill to our kestrel, who spends most of his working days hovering silently over the hay-stacks waiting for an unfortunate mouse to emerge and take the air. He homes on the tiniest of movements in grass or hedge, and swoops for the kill. He is the only creature who has been at work each and every day since we have had this little farm and I would not want to harm him either. So no poison.

This leaves cunning as my only weapon. Undeterred by my aged farming tomes which depressingly record, 'the extermination of rats is a task which must now be considered beyond the powers of civilised man', I am determined to bring them to heel. Here is my plan, culled from a farmer who found this suicidal method of rat-catching irresistible.

You take a barrel and place it in the middle of the barn. Into this you pour a seductive mixture of wheat, chaff, oats, barley and any other luscious grain until you have created a rat's Christmas dinner. You provide him with a ramp so that he can easily climb to the rim and quietly feast. Each day you replace what he has eaten until he is convinced that all his dreams have come true. Then, on the seventh day, remove the corn and replace it with a foot of water. Hungry, horrid little Ratty will toddle up the ramp tucking his napkin into his collar in eager anticipation and, blinded by his appetite, plunge into the icy wet and very deadly depths. If the barrel is deep enough he will not clamber out. Bye, bye, Ratty.

If it sounds far-fetched, I am told that the first time the inventive farmer employed the method he caught sixty rats in one night. Next week I shall try it but until then, every time I walk past the corn-stack I sing to myself 'Roll out the barrel, Let's have a barrel of fun'. It is just to lull them into a false sense of security. Cunning, eh?

I WISH TO ANNOUNCE a major breakthrough in vermin control. It is reasonably friendly from the environment's point of view, effective on a daily basis and costs nothing. The deterrent arrives around half past eight, does its work, and that sees us through to the following day, when once again it works its magic.

The device is a red van with the words 'Royal Mail' painted down the side. This vehicle is, in effect, the lethal bullet; but it is its deadly contents which do the fatal damage. Ever since I wrote in this newspaper that our entire stocks of corn and hay were being ravaged by rats, my mail has bulged with murderous little notes and word has spread along the ditches, dykes and field-drains of the rat community that readers of *The Times* are not to be trifled with. Our cowardly rats now sit and tremble in their burrows knowing that every visit from the postman arms me with more murderous ammunition to point in their direction. Some of your suggestions are quite wicked – at least, the best ones are.

We made the first attack on our rat population when we threshed the stack of corn. In the weeks before Christmas when the weather took an early turn for the worse, the hungry rats were quick to abandon their muddy summer quarters and set up home in our wheat. Our towering stacks of corn became the Dolphin Square of the rodent world, with unlimited food in every direction, warmth, shelter and even a thatched roof to keep out the rain. But as we removed the sheaves one by one to feed the threshing machine, Ratty sensed his world crumbling around him. Rather than make a quick exit, he foolishly headed for the basement so that by the time the stack was reduced to three feet in height, there was probably more rat than corn in it. Then we wrapped it in wire-netting and phoned a neighbour who owns a couple of evil little terriers. These, in anticipation of a little sport, had been living on reduced rations for a couple of days. I will not describe the mayhem that ensued but suffice it to say that two terriers were more than a match for fifty rats. The contest did not even go to a second round.

But a couple of months have passed, the weather has closed in, and once again disgusting little claw-like footprints are beginning to emerge from the ditch. Suspecting that I might have fired all my ammunition, Ratty, who may have forgotten that several methods of destruction arrive in every post, may be tempted to stage an invasion. He would be well advised to think again.

Mr Ford of Norfolk has written to tell me that his county boasts a pack of Rat Hounds and if I have any more trouble I should invite them to pay a call. He chillingly tells me that as a result of just one devastating visit to a farm, 520 rats met their end.

Another suggestion came from a farmer in Nottinghamshire and I am very reluctant to quote him for, although as far as I know there is no pressure group lobbying for a fairer deal for rats, there may be after this. I quote:

> First, check fire insurance on farm buildings. Set a trap to catch a live rat. Soak/spray rear ends of one or two rats (leather gloves advised for this part of the operation) in some flammable liquid – diesel/paraffin. NOT petrol. Light the rat and keep hold of it until the flames have died down and the scorching is well progressed. Release live (and very vocal) rat into stack area, preferably still smoking. Wave goodbye to all his friends and relatives as they depart for a quieter hotel.

And probably bid him farewell too. I would like to make it clear that I am not advocating this method or planning to try it, merely reporting a suggestion that has been made and that reflects, more perhaps than the sentimental country weekender may like, the way farmers get to feel about rats. My preferred method is the one I previously described which invited the rat to climb a plank which led him to a sodden death in a barrel of water. Mr Cook, who writes from Reading, thinks a little oil poured on the troubled waters in the barrel might help. He recently changed the oil in his Metro and left the full bowl overnight. He was rewarded with two dead mice. The letters keep on coming.

Another tells me that a high-tech device is now available which emits high-pitched whistles. This is said to put mortal fear into any whiskered beast within range. Assuming that your letters continue to flood in I intend to experiment on a variation of this method. I shall set up a loudspeaker and play 'Postman Pat' at full volume across the farmyard. It will save on matches.

I HAVE SPENT the week being slagged off from two directions: the first was entirely my own fault. It is time for potatoes to be planted and having had two successive years of growing spuds the size of ping-pong balls (albeit very tasty ones), I have a grotesque ambition to grow potatoes large enough to require two strong men to lift each of them. Just to prove that I can. So I have been spreading slag, and a filthy job it is, although not as disgusting as it used to be.

Slag was a widely used fertiliser until manufactured chemicals took over. It was a by-product of steel-making, removed from the fury of the blast-furnaces to end its days being carted by horses to tranquil fields. Here it was spread to enrich the land, and is reputed to have revitalised poor clay soils and returned exhausted pastures to fertile swards.

But a heavy price was paid by the men who did the spreading. Basic slag has a texture half-way between black powder paint and soot. The old-timers tell me it used to cling fiercely to skin, eyes and nostrils and a day's work forking it from the back of a cart as the horse trundled forward left ruddy-faced countrymen as black as chimney sweeps.

I had an easier time of it. With the demise of large-scale steel-making, basic slag became scarce. The organic farmer, however, seeking a naturally occurring source of phosphates to balance his soil, has a modern equivalent called Redzzlag. This is altogether more user-friendly; it is dusty but not annoyingly so, and although it seems to work its way into the very filling of your sandwiches it has none of the permanently colouring effects of its predecessor. If you have to be slagged off, it is as pleasant a way as any.

But the slagging-off that I took from another direction was more hurtful and came completely by surprise. Two letters arrived in last

Wednesday's post, both adding to the national debate that has been running in my column over the killing of pestilential rats. I intend to draw this discussion to a close, at least for this season. But not before I have quoted from these two contrasting letters.

One was from a chap who remembered the killing of rats at threshing time as a 'major social occasion'. He described how dogs were brought from miles around to slay rats entrapped by wire mesh as they fled the diminishing corn-stacks. He adds, 'Should the flow of rats slacken, there was always the chance of a spirited dog-fight as a diversion.' I have had many letters along these lines and many ingeniously cruel suggestions, which reached a climax recently with a full diagram showing a fiendishly lethal device constructed out of a shotgun and a sheet of corrugated iron. We will draw a veil over that one.

Then came a surprising letter from the Farm and Food Society, which caused me to rock back on my heels, for both of us sit firmly on the same side of the fence. They are a charity in favour of 'Humane, Wholesome and Fair Farming'. I could not agree more with their ambitions, but on rats I find them suspect. They invite me to take a charitable and humane view and quote a chapter from Konrad Lorenz's *On Aggression* in which he discusses rodent behaviour: '. . . The tenderness which characterises the relation of mammal mothers to their children extends in the case of rats not only to their fathers, but to all grandparents, uncles, aunts, cousins and so on.' It is eye-watering stuff. If Ratty had hired Sir Tim Bell to do a PR job on him, he could not have done better than this. 'The larger ones good-humouredly allow the smaller ones to take pieces of food away from them.'

I resisted spitting the words, 'Yes, but it's my livestock's hard-won food that they have nicked in the first place!' I tried to take an open-minded view. Perhaps the Farm and Food Society are right and Ratty is a nice guy, after all. I was further softened by the lady who wrote with passion: 'How can you sleep at night knowing that rats might be dying?' Anyway, I can postpone a final decision because, as I paced the field behind the horse-drawn fertiliser spreader, I noticed that the muddy tracks which lead from the ditch to the barns have started to grass over. The rats have gone away for the summer.

But I did notice one thing. On my bag of Redzzlag was the name of the source. It is the menacingly titled *Black Hole Mine* in the village of Eyam, in Derbyshire. School history lessons will remind you that it was this village which bravely went into voluntary isolation to prevent further spread of the Black Death when it became clear that fleas carried by rats had brought the deadly disease to the village. I have no wish needlessly to slag him off, but Ratty – kind though he is to his grandparents – must carry his share of the blame for the death of countless humans down the centuries. Ah well. He is safe on this farm for now, I suppose. Until next winter, anyway.

I HAVE DECIDED to follow the fashionable lead of the Hollywood stars and renounce violence. After I wrote of a method of frightening rats from the farm by setting fire to the rear end of one and hurling him at the others, I cannot say I was overwhelmed by letters of revulsion, but one letter was enough. From now on there will be no more gratuitous violence on this little farm. If you should ever happen to see my name linked with a project bearing the title *Silence of the Lambs*, you can rest assured it will be a veterinary video on ovine laryngitis.

Not that there is all that much violence, anyway. I have always thought that the animals here are much more cruel to me than I ever could be to them. I admit that when we load pigs into the trailer the palm of my hand has occasionally come firmly to rest on the rumps of the truculent litter; but it is more of a guiding touch than a deliberate attempt at coercion. I have learned that pigs cannot be made to do anything by force which they are not inclined to do. In my days as a pig-handling novice I was advised to grab them by the ears while someone else got the tail, and shunt them around that way. It never really worked. No human grasp can match the wriggling capacity of the pig which, when coupled with the piercing squeal, makes the whole operation into a nightmare Hollywood would be hard pressed to beat. Nowadays I use a bucket. I fill it with swill, lay it in whichever direction I wish the pig to go and, sooner or later, the pig will follow. It never fails. I might be there for five minutes or fifty, but sooner or later greed will overtake all other instincts and the reluctant hog will budge.

And that is the non-violent way it is going to be in the future. Even my arch enemies the rats will only have themselves to blame for their demise, for I have decided to follow a reader's kind suggestion and allow them to commit suicide. I mentioned that I had been advocating a barrel filled with water, tasty oats floating on the surface, and a ramp up which the rodent could climb. But a kind reader suggests covering the top of the barrel with brown paper and sprinkling the bait on that for a week. Then, one day, take a razor-blade and cut slits in the paper. On Ratty's next visit he will find the floor of his restaurant rather uncertain, and before he knows where he is he will be in the basement swimming pool from which there is no escape. It will be all his own fault. No more chasing rats round the barn in futile attempts to hit them with a stick.

So how am I to fill the time which has now become vacant since I have decided the farm is going to be run in future by gentle persuasion? I am turning to art. I am taking up the brush and intend by next autumn to have created a masterpiece. It will be on display by the roadside, some time in November. It is the huge threshing machine, which I have decided is in urgent need of a coat of paint. Last autumn a kind owner of a steam engine offered to come and power it for us; overcome by the romance of the thing, I agreed. But imagine my shame as our dowdy, down-at-heel threshing drum had to stand next to his sparkling, radiant engine in her proud livery of green, black and red. I cannot allow such shame to fall on this farm again.

But my problem, and excuse for not having done this job before, is that I am baffled as to where to get hold of the paint. Any old paint will not do, for this is a Ransome's Threshing Machine and was painted in a particularly vivid and famous shade of pink. It might seem an odd colour for a piece of farm machinery but pink was not all that rare. Farm waggons were often done in it, and the inside of our shepherd's hut is painted a rich shade of pink. Farmers were a good century ahead of Sir Terence Conran when it came to style. But finding the right shade of pink is not a simple matter of taking a small sample and going to a paint shop and having it mixed; for the colour of our machine has been achieved after forty years of weathering and it is impossible to guess what it was like when first applied.

It seems almost certain that in a country which has apparently been stockpiling tons of biscuits in the event of nuclear war, there should not be one farmer who did not stash away several gallons of Ransome's Pink Paint just in case the holocaust should scorch his threshing tackle. If such a farmer exists, he knows where to find me. Just drop a line to the pacifist pinko, care of this newspaper.

7

Man Versus Machine

(And a Young Horse to Add to the Confusion)

THEY SAY THAT a little knowledge is a dangerous thing, but in my short farming experience I have found exactly the reverse. It is often a single small piece of knowledge that saves the day.

An example surfaced this week when I decided that in the interests of tidiness and good husbandry some long grass in the meadows needed topping. I had a choice of several ways of doing it: I could harness the horses to the clipper, get out the noisy petrol-driven strimmer, or be true to my vintage farming ambitions and unearth the scythe.

I rejected the horses on the grounds that the area to be cut was small and, anyway, it would take as much effort to bring the horses into the stable, harness them and walk them to the meadow as it would to cut each blade of grass with nail scissors. This left the strimmer and the scythe.

So why, against all my natural inclinations, did I nearly opt for the stinking strimmer? Especially when I have in the barn a gleaming new scythe with a steam-bent handle and finely honed blade stamped with the essential words 'Made in Sheffield'? The answer is that, much as I have tried to develop a working relationship with this primitive instrument, I had so far failed to get the slightest hint of a tune out of it. I have taken it into long grass and weeds and slashed from side to side in a rhythmical manner, twisting at the waist and shuffling forwards like a young hopeful in a *Come Dancing* contest. Yet although I have achieved a considerable sweat on my brow, I have so far failed to mow much grass. It simply does not look as though it has been cut. Tufts of grass are dragged out but that is not mowing. I dreamed of a whistling slice through the vegetation, an even depth of cut and a song on my lips: 'One man went to mow, went to mow a meadow . . .' Mark the word *mow*. Not mangle.

I have two sources of reference when faced with a dilemma such as this. One is Derek, himself something of a vintage item. All he could offer was advice given to him by a gypsy: if you ever slice yourself with the blade you must piddle on the cut and you will live happily ever after.

My other source of reference is my collection of aged farming tomes but, even here, advice was scarce, although a 1914 edition of *Fream's Elements of Agriculture* offered the following:

> The early part of the stroke is easily made . . . but as material collects it becomes more difficult to finish the stroke. Young beginners make the end of the stroke with the left hand too far in advance of the left leg (which should be a little in the rear of the right). After the first half of the stroke, the left hand should be drawn sharply round and near to the left leg . . .

On reading this, I remembered a teach-yourself-ballroom-dancing aid which had white foot-prints on a black carpet and was rolled out to help its pupil learn the Military Two Step. Then I thought that perhaps my action was not at fault and it was simply the blade that was not sharp enough. I took a carborundum stone and rubbed each side firmly but, as the text-book dictates, flatly along the side so as not to dull the edge. Alas, as I made my vigorous stroke, I did not allow for the curve of the blade and soon had blood running from finger-tip to elbow. I remembered the gypsy's advice but as I was quite close to the lane at the time I had to decide whether to incur his displeasure by favouring Elastoplast, or risk a charge of indecent exposure. In the end, I went home for tea.

'Have you got the hang of that scythe?' chortled Derek on his next visit, knowing full well that I would not. 'I'll show yer!' he boasted, and lifted the scythe from its hook in the barn. 'Well, I can see what's wrong. You ain't got a grass nail. That won't work without a grass nail!'

Now I thought there were two parts to a scythe: the curved wooden handle called a snath, or snaith, and the blade. Apparently not. Across the angle made between the two is a short rod, the length of a strong nail, which prevents the blade from twisting away from the grass which is being cut. It is not more than three or four inches long and thinner than a pencil but vital to the whole operation. I contacted the Sheffield makers of the scythe and as soon as the grass nail was fitted, the scythe found its tune. It had the full-bodied feel of an entire orchestra. I swung, and mowed, and sang. The scythe and I could have danced all night.

So now you know the importance of the grass nail in the operation of the scythe, and those of a nervous disposition can put the knowledge to good use. Should you be haunted by visions of the Grim Reaper, check to see if his nail is in place and if you should find it missing you have little to fear.

I HAVE BEEN FOLLOWING the saga of the beleaguered BBC and its attempts to salvage the scum from what should have been a frothing lather of suds surrounding its latest soap opera, *Eldorado*; and I have to say that I have every sympathy. I, too, am in the middle of launching my own annual soap opera, a tragicomic saga of one man's attempts to come to terms with a devious item of aged farm machinery. And I'm not getting any applause either. Yes, it is harvest time: the dreaded binder has been dragged from the dark recesses of the barn to face the pitiless sun. Episode one goes like this.

With his soul overflowing with enthusiasm and optimism, our ever-ageing hero decides that he will approach the binder this year in a state of total relaxation. He will not repeat last year's errors of shouting at it, hitting it and kicking it. Rather, he will calmly persuade it to work, tend it and caress it. His placidity, he hopes, will be repaid.

Regular readers of my *Times* column will by now have amassed sufficient knowledge of antique farm machinery to qualify for at least a doctorate in the subject, but in case any of you are unfamiliar with a binder I can best describe it as a device which cuts the standing corn, wraps it into bundles, throws a length of string around them, knots it and throws the parcel on to the ground. These bundles are called sheaves and make grown men go misty-eyed with nostalgia at harvest festivals. But the mechanical process which produces them can descend, at any turn of the cog, into chaos. Uneasily the viewer becomes aware of this lurking menace in the summer sunshine.

Having established the main characters, i.e. myself and the binder, we then introduce the juvenile lead, a young lad who drives the tractor. I know we usually do things with horses round here but the binder is a heavy bit of gear and we do not have sufficient horses to haul it. In the opening scenes (not to be shown before nine o'clock), he stands by as I caress the machine with oil, pack her nipples with grease, tighten the belts on her canvases and generally show all the signs of a man if not exactly in love, then at least expecting some kind of fulfilment. Anticipating his oats, you might say.

Then, cut to a more sombre scene with threatening music as I look with horror at the corn. Instead of standing high and proud like oats should, mine have been dashed to the ground by high winds and torrential rain. Instead of a forest, I have a carpet. It is the nightmare scenario, for although the knife will cut the stalks, the corn is unable to fall into the jaws of the machine; so it lies, doggo and unharvestable. Cue commercial break.

Part two starts with our hero losing his nerve, thinking he will ring a man with a nice, shiny combine-harvester and retire to a hammock in the garden while modern machinery works its magic. But his principles surface, he sets his jaw and with grim determination decides to go on. He steers the binder at the corn and gives the signal for the young driver to give it all he's got. In triumph they progress all of three feet before there is a mighty jam-up, the poor machine bursting at the seams with tangled stalks. But they press on. When wooden parts of the machine shatter, they stop and with increasingly violent blows, carve new ones from nearby pieces of wreckage. The conveying canvases stretch under the load and are savagely tightened. Nothing will stop these men. It is epic. It reminds one of a Norse saga.

Then the final tragic scene. In an absent-minded moment when both tractor driver and binder operator should have been watching where they were going, they manage effortlessly to drive the whole paraphernalia into a tree. It was an overhanging branch that winged us, shattering a vital cog into two useless halves and effectively writing out the binder in episode one. The machine lies silent, the harvest doomed.

Are you on the edge of your seat yet? If not, you soon will be, for I rang my ever-useful neighbour Farmer White to crave his advice. Here the plot thickens; for he knows an engineer of the old school, ideal to carry out such a repair. But he is a retired man and will only work for a chosen few. Will he come, or won't he? Will the corn go to waste as the broken binder sits, forlorn, in the corner of the field? Cue titles, over a close-up of throbbing veins in my temple.

There you are. Surely a whole nation would be gripped by such a saga. I suggest the poor devils who have been detailed off to save *Eldorado* should come here for a couple of weeks to find out what real drama is all about. I can promise you that at this stage in the farming year I would be only too happy to swap places with them. Sitting in a folding chair with a chilled beer shouting, 'Sooper darling, just one more time, luv,' has got real appeal.

The good news is that he said yes, he would come. He would have been far happier tending his bursting vegetable garden and enjoying his retirement, but for the sake of my increasingly urgent harvest he would 'see what he could do'. He arrived with his spanners – rather surgically I thought – in a washing-up bowl. It was appropriate. I am not squeamish about blood, but to me the sight of a broken cog the size of a dinner-plate had been almost too gruesome to behold. I nearly fainted. In fact, the night before I had a dream in which visions of mutilation, blood and cogs were all interwoven.

But my mechanic had the stomach for it. He reached for a hammer, weighed it in his hand and then settled for a heavier one. He tapped. Then he tapped again a little harder and still nothing moved. This was not good: we had to take the thing off before attempting a repair, and since cog had been married to shaft for sixty glorious years it was going to take a mighty blow to effect a divorce. At least, that is how I would have done it; I would have found the heaviest blunt instrument I could lift and simply pounded the immovable gear into submission. This, of course, would have caused even more damage; which is why the mechanic opted for a lighter hammer and tapped in the opposite direction. They were not wild, undirected blows; every impact counted until the joyous moment when the cog came free and I could whisk it away to the blacksmith who thought he might manage a repair.

But the joy on my face was nothing compared with the delight on the mechanic's when he had hit it and put the hammer back quietly into its bowl. Here was a piece of machinery that belonged to an age with which he could relate. Modern farm machinery, although infinitely more effective than my aged gear, has a menace about it. It is dangerous stuff which can mangle a man in a minute without even pausing. It runs at high speeds and is so heavy that only a powerful tractor can move it. On the other hand, horse-drawn gear ticks over so slowly that grease and oil seem hardly necessary; and there are very few items on this farm that two of us cannot trundle out of the way if we need to.

Things, they say, come in threes. Later that afternoon we were to add a third beaming face to our two happy ones. With the cog expertly welded and the binder once again about to reap the corn, an elderly face appeared over the farm gate. This is not an unusual occurrence here, for as soon as the horses are jingling along, the threshing machine humming or the binder clattering, the sound is a clarion call to relics of a previous age. Some old men come to admire and enjoy sights they remember from their youth; harder cases will stare witheringly at your furrows with criticism written plainly across their faces. In most of the traditional farming techniques which we employ there are a hundred different things to get right, and if you have only mastered ninety-nine of them they will notice it. And mention it.

But it was not a critical face that appeared over the gate. It was an old boy simply longing once again to get up on that binder seat and cut a few swathes through the corn as he had last done forty years ago. It must have been like rediscovering a train set from one's childhood. He strode across with a new alacrity in his step and eagerly accepted my invitation to 'have a few rounds off'. 'My ol' dad use t' say, "'Y' can't cut corn with a binder when the sun don't shine,"' he told us. We looked at the cloudy sky but decided to press on. And I am glad we did, for the smile on his face outshone anything the sun could have produced that afternoon.

Good old binder. This time last week I wanted to scrap it as no more than a grumpy tangle of canvas, iron and cogs, rightfully obsolete these forty years. Today it has made two good men happy. I reprieve it: it can live to break my heart another year.

I T IS QUITE COMMON on this farm for us to indulge in out-moded agricultural practices; but when we are employing techniques described in a book published in 1865 as being 'antique and primitive', there is an uneasy feeling of having stepped further back into time than is quite safe. But I had no alternative. We have a towering stack of sheaves of corn which, once threshed to remove the grains from the straw, will be ready to be sold. My prospective customer, a miller, asked for a mere half-hundredweight of the corn for testing.

There were two ways of fulfilling his request, the first being to set up the threshing machine. But this is not to be taken lightly. This magnificent creature demands time to manoeuvre it into position alongside the stack, the best part of a morning to oil and grease her innermost parts, and six or seven men to feed her with sheaves, catch the grain, handle the straw and bag up the chaff. To put all those wheels into motion for a single bag of corn would be like setting up the scenery for Wagner's *Ring* and then only singing the final chorus. Anyway, the threshing machine has a long and convoluted intestine which takes some filling, and the modest number of sheaves I was contemplating threshing would hardly provide enough flow to get any corn out of the other end.

So I decided that we would flail the corn. We would spread it out on the barn floor and hit it severely with a stick till it was forced to yield its precious grain. But where to find a flail and, more importantly, a man who knew how to use it? A flail, research revealed, is a hinged stick usually of ash or thorn; one part is five feet long and held in the hand, the other part, about three feet long, does the beating. The two are hinged with a thong of untanned leather or preferably eelskin. Nor is it merely a matter of 'flailing around' which has come to mean wild, haphazard movements. 'Four or five women', I read, 'range themselves in a circle upon their knees and beat in short sharp strokes following one another in rapid succession around the circle.'

Alas, I have never been the kind of man who has four or five women always handy. All I had was my friend Dilly. Nor did I have time to hunt eels or cut ash, so we used sticks. Nor does our barn have the dimensions of a cathedral, like the one described by Thomas Hardy with 'a wooden threshing floor in the centre formed of thick oak, black with age and polished by the beating of flails for many generations'. But, nevertheless, as we bent to the ground, barn doors open to allow the breeze to disperse the chaff and cool our brows, time slipped backwards a century and a half.

We hit till our arms ached but the rate at which the grain flowed was pitifully slow. 'How much d' yer want?' asked Dilly after half an hour. 'Four stone,' I replied. 'Are you jokin'?' he replied. 'There's about a cupful on that floor.'

I never believed that upper arm muscles had so much ache in them. I tried flailing standing upright with the corn on the ground; then to ease the pain I knelt and held the sheaf in the other hand so that at least I was encouraged to continue by the sight of bullets of grain hitting the ground. However, hit them too hard and the grain bounced off the sheet and into the dark corners of the barn to be devoured by mice. Every ten minutes we swept the cloth, poured the corn into a sack and put it on to the scales. After two hours we reached the two stone mark. Half-way there.

I read that the flail had many local names; it was sometimes a 'stick-and-a-half', a 'drashel' or a 'Joseph-and-Mary'. More to the point I further read that men working in pairs should keep up a strike rate of thirty flails per minute producing twelve bushels of wheat a day. A bushel is about sixty-five pounds, so our achievement of half a hundredweight in less than four hours, was quite respectable.

Four hours of this work was as much as I fancied. It is well to remember that this was usually the work of two men for the entire winter; and when the mechanical threshing machines came to rob them of their labour, they would roam in gangs seeking to destroy them.

But on the basis of one afternoon's experience, ours need not fear the lighted match. Nor must we delve too far into farming tradition, for we soon discover that those who lived it were greater men than we. I do not think we shall repeat the flailing experience. As Dilly said as he headed for home, 'Too much slap, and not enough tickle.'

W ITH OUR YOUNG cart-horse, Prince, approaching his fourth birthday we have decided it is time for him to join the workforce. He has had four good years of growing and the time has now come to elevate him from being merely a good-looking horse to a useful one.

Standing in the stable, unaccustomed to his harness, his eyes dart from side to side and confused thoughts clearly cross his mind. He has no fear because he has already been taught the basics of what he must do, but he is still a child and shifts from foot to foot like a boy at a new school.

A cart-horse is first broken in when it is two. It learns to pull light loads, feel the weight of the leather collar press against its shoulders, and accept that the jangle of chains behind is no cause for fear. But two is too young for a full day's work, and so it is turned out on to meadows for another two years, then taught the final lessons. By this time a horse has developed its full strength and, if the breaking had been entirely left till now, it could well be too headstrong to learn anything at all.

All this I have learnt from Mrs Cheryl Clark of Stoke-by-Nayland who has broken all the horses we use on our farms. She is a compact but powerful lady to whom no man or goose would dare say boo, and from whom no young cart-horse has failed to learn the required lessons. She once fell beneath a pair of frightened, bolting, young heavy horses. She was mercilessly cut and trampled, but to ensure her muscles did not seize she merely rested for a short time and then went out to plough with two more horses for the rest of the day. I feel safe with a horse that has been taught its manners by Cheryl.

Yet I am sure that young Prince knows that I am made of lesser stuff. He will no doubt test me all the time. I shall tell him to 'whooah' and he might not, and then I shall have to be certain to make him; otherwise he will know that I am putty in his hands. A cart-horse that does not do precisely as told is of no use on a farm. Pet ponies in Jilly Cooper novels may get away with murder, but when an animal weighs a tonne, it has to play it your way for everyone's safety.

Derek, my old horseman friend, came along for Prince's first day's work. We harnessed him, took him to the meadow and hitched him to a light sledge. 'G'up!' The horse leaned purposefully into his collar and trudged along. It would take no expert to spot that he was a young 'un, for he drifted in a youthful, gangly way like a conscript who has not yet learned to march straight. The steady plodding will come with maturity.

I made the first mistake, not Prince. I crept into the field too quietly just as Derek turned to drive him in the other direction. He caught an unfamiliar sight out of the corner of his eye. Again I was reminded of a schoolchild on its first day, just getting settled when something unexpected comes up. Where a child would burst into tears, a horse bolts. Prince broke into a trot and a sweat as he swung round, confused by the turning and the pulling which he had not done for several months. Then he tensed his body, clearly intent on galloping to the horizon. Derek, who was standing on the sledge, hung on. He pulled first on one rein and then the other, till the confused and panting horse came to a halt. When the horse had settled and was standing once more happily to attention, he told me a tale.

'I wuz' rakin' hay with a three-year-old mare, years ago. I saw an ol' partridge and chicks in the grass and thought that by the time we came down the field agin, they would be out of the way. Well, the' wuzn't. That old bird she flew up when she saw that hoss and hit that hoss right under the belly. Well! That hoss, she took off across the field, jumped a ditch, broke the shafts, went straight through a blackthorn hedge and galloped for another ten minutes before I caught her. Well, I went to see the guv'nor. "I'll get rid of that mare," he said, "she ain't no use." I said that it wasn't the hoss's fault and do you know what I did? I put her back in shafts, drove her out to the field and raked another thirteen acres with her. She weren't no trouble after that.'

We did the same with Prince. Let him settle, twitched the reins, told him to 'G'up'. He moved forward as if he had done it for a decade. He marched confidently around the farm and after half an hour we paired him with our oldest horse, Star, and hitched them to the harrows. They pulled the spiky combs through the soil till an acre or two had been crumbled and Prince ambled back to his stable to enjoy what was probably the best meal of his life. The young horse had finished his first day's work on the farm.

I HEAR FROM French astrologers that this coming Tuesday a turbulent conjunction of planets will spawn natural disaster on a grand scale. I beg to disagree – it was actually last weekend. I do not know if the earth moved for you but never before in my farming career have I lived through such a day of continuous turmoil. Whatever influences were at work they infiltrated their evil into every beast and every square inch of land on this farm.

It started well; a cracking day for drilling the corn. The sticky land had dried nicely throughout the week and we went to work with the harrows. By Sunday, a touch of frost had reduced the soil to a perfect tilth or 'mould' as they say round here, and I rang Derek the horseman. We decided not only to drill the field, but to give Prince his first full day's work. Farmer Jolly, who worked this land forty years ago with horses, always used to warn that whatever the job, '. . . that won't come right if yer does it on a Sunday'. I shall never doubt his wisdom again.

We hauled the seed drill to the field, fighting the blustery cold wind every inch of the way. This wind nagged, tugged and teased the horses with its cutting edge and roared in their ears till they were unable to hear commands; so they guessed at what they were being told. This leads to loss of temper on both sides.

Prince was fit to burst. Although well broken to harness, he has yet to be schooled in everyday farm work. And so, whereas our old soldiers Star and Blue backed up to the seed drill in perfect order, Prince pranced and danced and had to be guided and cajoled every inch of the way. 'Whooah, boy. Stand still . . .' we shouted above the gale which, rattling in his ears, confused him even more.

When they were finally hooked to the machine, Derek ordered the team to step forward. The untutored Prince lunged; his tender years had not taught him that the slow and steady approach is always more productive. There was a loud crack and all three horses shot forward as if from a gun. A cast-iron part of the drill had shattered, leaving the machine behind and the horses going ever faster down the field. We all ran, but Derek held on. Star and Blue would not have flinched at such a common mishap but the new boy in the class had put everyone's nerves on edge.

We calmed the horses and set about repairs. We hooked the team to the drill and were about to take a further step forward when out of the corner of my eye I saw a chilling sight. Galloping across the meadow like a motorised iceberg was our white cow Sage with her snowball of a calf and all the other cows and bullocks storming behind. The gate to the cattle yard had blown open and the stock had seized the chance of a quick mid-winter away-day. I dashed to close the gates before they could escape any further and left Derek holding the team of horses. By the time I returned, relations had deteriorated. Prince, bursting with nervous energy, had reared in the air and crashed down, splitting his harness as he hit the ground. I was on the point of tears. Derek said nothing, which is always a bad sign.

I trudged back to the farm-yard with Prince and his broken harness to be met by white-faced children. 'The pony's got out!' was the news. Apparently, before deciding to opt for a vacation in the meadow, our escaped white cow and her followers had toured the estate putting the fear of God into every creature. This was confirmed by a number of frolicsome hoofmarks. The pigs loftily ignored her but the pony, never having seen such a beast before, took fright and vaulted a substantial fence. My wife caught it and stumped past me hauling it on a piece of rope with the look of a woman interrupted half-way through the Sunday papers. In sombre mood I headed once again into the wind in the direction of Derek who was now drilling with two horses.

Things changed after dinner. Presumably Mercury moved into Uranus, or something. A much calmer Prince joined the other two horses on the seed drill and all three plodded the length of the field as if they had been working together all their lives. As dusk fell, we drilled the last round of the wheat and men and horses, equally exhausted by the tensions of the day, stumbled home. I spotted the new moon in the sky with Venus clear and bright above the barn, and thanked the stars for releasing their frustrating grip upon us. Derek looked at Prince, sweaty and panting. 'That young hoss, he's got a fair old lather between his legs today.' Mmm, I thought, he's not the only one.

8
Endless Torment

I BET THAT I only have to mention that we are currently making hay, with cart-horses, for some of you to swoon. There is something about this potent combination of images which turns grown men and women soppy and forces them into making rash promises – 'We'd love to help, just give us a ring' – which are hardly ever fulfilled.

But perhaps it is just as well. If they were to arrive with their hearts full of enthusiasm they would surely go home with them broken. I am sorry to say that there is little in hay-making which fulfils the golden promise of lazy, hazy days under a beating sun and stolen kisses under the stack by night.

The rural literature of the forties and fifties is probably to blame. This was the period when the tractor was finally in charge, the horse on his last legs and creeping nostalgia starting to eclipse the memory of the sheer bloodiness of making hay. To quote one example, 'Haymaking, or haysel, is a joyous time . . . the most exhilarating of farming occasions . . . haysel was a yearly picnic . . . little children turned out to make merry . . . the cuckoo's call comes fresh across the meadow.' Well, I have made hay in the old-fashioned way for a mere four years now, but on the basis of my experience and conversations with old men who used to toil at this annual 'picnic', very few haysels are remembered with much affection.

This year's has certainly been one to forget. It started promisingly with a lush crop of grass that flourished through the wet, thundery weather of a few weeks ago. Then the hint of a settled spell of drying winds and hot sunshine, made me drag the horse-drawn clipper from the shed.

It had not mown ten yards of grass when a depressingly loud crack guaranteed that no more would be mown that day. The cutting knife had shattered. Now, it is no problem to get a spare for a modern mower; but ours is fifty years old and I could spend a whole year turning over junk heaps and rummaging through auctions before I found another blade. Thankfully, Farmer White was generous enough to spend the whole of a hot Sunday morning welding together the steel jigsaw. I didn't have the heart to tell him that no sooner was the knife back in business than the wooden swingletree to which the horses are attached splintered into shards of worm-eaten wood at the first hint of 'G'up'.

Somehow we got around the six-acre field, almost. With a tiny postage-stamp of grass left standing, the mower came to another depressing halt. The irritating patch was just too large to be ignored. I got out the garden shears and in a vile temper, cut it down. Romantic passers-by gazed approvingly over the hedge. I swore at them.

This was the moment when the weather turned its face against me. The forecasts of sunny, settled spells gave way to hints of showers. But I pressed on regardless, turning the grass with our vintage rake till it was nearly dry, picking up bundles and twisting them between my hands to see if they might be dry enough to stack, contemplating the sweaty work of pitching all this dry grass on to the waggon and building a hay-stack.

The whole operation was made even more depressing by the sight of modern hay-making on a field on the other side of the farm. I decided that we had so much grass this year that it was beyond what I could manage, so modern machinery had to be brought in. It never gives me any pleasure to see a tractor on this land; it drowns the atmosphere, disturbs the peace, and sets a thundering pace to which we are not attuned. It is even more irritating to see it charging along with its powerful mower cutting seven acres in a few hours while we are still bent double in the long grass trying to find a vital bit of chain.

Of course, there is no reason why we could not have cut the whole lot with the horses eventually. But the costs of hiring men to do the stacking and carting – jobs hardly anyone wants to do – would make it the most expensive hay in Britain. I take some comfort that this is not a novel problem. Writing his *Farmer's Year* in 1899, J. Rider Haggard bemoans the fact that he 'can scarcely afford to put so much labour into the land which will not pay the price'.

So we are doing as much as we can afford and all we ask is to be given a break. Every soaking robs the mown grass of a little of its goodness and even if it should spoil completely and turn rank and mouldy, we shall still have the gloomy job of carting the mess off the field. And as I write the chilly wind is whipping up more rain-laden clouds. Some picnic.

I NEVER THOUGHT it possible that such a distinguished countryman's journal as *The Field* would ever publish photographs of a titillating and arousing nature. However, a few weeks ago, I opened my copy to find a picture which would send any aspiring vintage farmer, like me, to the cold shower.

It was a photograph of a man with a pair of horses, drawing ridges of earth with his plough. By inspired use of lenses and landscape the photographer had miniaturised the man and his team to give the effect of a Lilliputian ploughing between rows of newly ironed corduroy.

It was neither the farmer nor his horses which kindled lustful thoughts within me. It was the furrows. Kinky they were not, but almost obscenely straight. They headed to the horizon with no hint of a meander, no suggestion of a wobble from the straight and narrow. They were perfectly formed, lying seductively across the land, inviting caress. My heart raced.

I was hardly into my farming-with-horses career when I discovered the tantalising nature of the straight line. All jobs in every field on this farm start with a single furrow, alongside which all other furrows will lie. If the first is not straight, the last can never be. If the furrows wobble, so will the seed drill when it sows the corn; and then the horse-drawn hoe will not be able to follow it because the hoe and the horse both work in straight lines. Even when it is a job where straightness is of no particular virtue, like rolling, it is inadvisable to let one's standards drop: you can bet there will be some old boy leaning over the gate, watching. He may not say anything at the time but sooner or later word will reach me that 'Ol' Charlie thought I wuz in a right muddle.'

In the days when all farms were worked with horses, it was considered a horseman's legitimate recreation to stroll along the lanes on a Sunday, peering over the hedges, noting the deficiencies in someone else's work. Each wobble was hauled out in evidence that night in the pub to shame the man who let his attention and his horses momentarily wander.

Only practice can make perfect; but the snag with rehearsing is that it all has to be done in public and it is irreversible. If I draw a furrow which rolls like the proverbial English road, I cannot fix a sign to it saying, 'Sorry, only done for practice.' Nor can I cover it up; it is too deep and permanent. That is the reason my heart pounds when I call to the horses, 'G'up,' and cut the initial furrow in a field.

This week it has pounded a lot. I have been drawing ridges into which I planted potatoes and it is exactly the same operation as was being performed by the farmer in that stimulating picture. But I fear that at the end of the day not even a trick photographer could have created such a powerful impression out of my pathetic efforts.

I used a ridging plough, known hereabouts as a 'tater tom'. It is similar to an ordinary plough but throws the earth to both sides leaving a V-shaped furrow. It is into that furrow you drop the seed potatoes, and then plough the length of the ridge to throw the soil back from whence it came. This not only covers the potato, it leaves a ridge of earth above it into which the young potatoes grow. If you find this difficult to follow, imagine what it is like to perform.

The first drawing of the furrows is easy, and even the dropping of the potatoes becomes pleasant if you do not allow your mind to dwell on the tedium of it. I once heard of an old horseman who, when asked what occupied his mind as he worked alone in the fields, replied with a twinkling eye, 'Same as any young man thinks about when he's on his own for long enough!' Me, I thought of that photograph, and lusted after the earthy mounds.

But when the climax came and I set the plough to create my mounds, my orderly field of spuds became a battleground. My 'tater tom' wandered hazily, like a besotted schoolboy overcome with his first thoughts of love. I wept, heartbroken. I cursed the plough, the horses and the spuds. Love turned to hate. Such beauty, I realised, is only found in the glossy pages of tantalising magazines and is beyond the reach of this common man. I do not want to live through such an unsettling experience again. The next time I am in the paper shop I am asking the newsagent to move *The Field* to the top shelf, out of reach of this impressionable youngster.

I F YOU KNOW any organic farmers, would you go out of your way to be pleasant to them? Especially at this time of year; for if my experience is anything to go by, the month of May is when the nervous breakdowns begin to sprout.

They are triggered by a single event. In my case, the sudden turn of the weather from cool April showers to searing hot summer days. Up till then I had found odd moments to sit in the shade of the ash tree by the pond, from where I could see the ever greener fields of wheat and oats, observe how well the lucerne was growing and rejoice in the first sproutings of the mangel-wurzels as faint green lines across the bare earth.

As long as what I saw between the plants *was* bare earth, I was happy. But the weather changed and so did the view, and it was not for the better. After the first couple of days of hot sunshine I found the farm daubed with green as if an artist had loaded his brush and spattered green paint across the entire holding. Where once there had been only young mangels there were thistles, mayweed and every other species of pest known to botanical science. Where straight lines of corn had once marched across bare fields, pink flowers appeared and closer examination revealed more thistles gathering for a major assault. Amid the thick sward of lucerne, repulsive rape had sprouted from dormant seed from a crop planted four years ago. And even in the closely grazed meadows, docks were beginning to show and the occasional deadly kind of thistle that has points too sharp for a man to grab.

The organic farmer has no enemy like the weed. It steals moisture and nutrients, and not content with starving its neighbouring plants, bullies and crowds them to death. Selective chemicals can kill them, but the organic farmer does not have the satisfaction of such swift and decisive revenge.

Instead, he frets. But we are perhaps in a better position than some, for the horse-drawn agriculture that we practise was evolved in pre-chemical days when there was no other option than to kill the weeds by sheer cunning. Some, like thistles, can make a good running but only over a short course. If you trip them at the right moment you can knock them out of the race for ever. On the subject of choosing your moment, the old farming rhyme goes:

> Cut 'em in May, they'll come next day.
> Cut 'em in June they'll come again soon.
> But cut 'em in July and they're sure to die!

We are armed not only with such wisdom but also with weapons which modern agriculture has foolishly allowed to slip into antiquity. Not many people believe that by using horses we can steer hoes between rows of corn. But we have done it two years running on this farm, taking twelve rows at a time and hoeing five acres in half a morning. I found the disused hoe in the bowels of a great barn and brought it back to life. In its revitalised state it now does a devastatingly murderous job on all types of weeds in all manner of crops. For the root crops, like turnips and mangels, we have an even simpler device called a scoop hoe, known hereabouts as a 'scuppoe'. This will destroy anything in its path and needs one man to steer and one to lead the horse. When the plant is of sufficient height for the rows to be clearly seen, a good horse will walk unaided between them.

So why the breakdown if I have the tools and horses to carry out the deadly job? Well, if it were only the weeds, things would be fine; but as the temperature rises so does the pressure. I think of the wicked flies and how the sheep must be dagged to remove the filth from their rear ends lest the fly lays its eggs here, which hatch into maggots and can eat the sheep alive. In the luscious lucerne the invasive rape is in flower and will shortly shed its seeds so that this year's minor problem becomes next year's major disaster. Docks and thistles must be cut around the field edges to prevent them shedding seed. Even the innocent lambs are now approaching an age where the boys and girls must not be allowed to share the same dormitory if gym-slip pregnancies are to be avoided. Sheep! Now suddenly it is even warm enough to shear. It may rain soon, so lucerne hay must quickly be made. A telephone call tells me the young sow has been served by the boar and is ready for collection. And oh, God, the potatoes are through and need earthing up. The grass has suddenly leaped a foot and is earthing the electric fences and the cows will escape . . .

Goodbye, pondside afternoons. It's summertime, and the living is far from easy.

I HAVE FOOLISHLY been looking at the other man's grass and as you might expect, it is much greener. So am I green, with envy. This confuses me, because I thought that being an organic farmer I was being as Green as I could be. The problem is that the Greener one's farming methods, the less likely you are to find your meadows as lush as the next man's at this crucial time of year. The demands of intensive farming do not allow the conventional farmer time to wait for the soil to warm and the clover and humus to work their fertilising magic. Instead, he must pour fertiliser from a bag; so that no sooner has it crossed the mind of the first swallow to head north, than his blades of grass are a foot long. So slender are farming profits these days that every ounce of goodness must be extracted from the land.

But the organic man is, to a certain extent, compensated for his patience. He knows that cows grazing over-fertilised swards are more likely to suffer mineral deficiencies and even die because of the changed chemical balance of the grasses. He knows, too, that the compost he has added to his land will act as a sponge and give up moisture through the long hot summer when less cared-for pastures will have been burnt like toast. Even so, when he looks across the hedge in the spring and sees his neighbour's grass twice the height of his, he suffers a test of his organic faith.

I have been testing myself, in Dorset. I walked part of the coastal path which rambles across the fertile downs where a combination of soil, southern warmth and maritime dampness creates a perfect country for growing grass. But good grass doesn't happen by accident. Even our prime minister underrates it. When asked on his celebrated visit to the BBC's desert island what his luxury would be, he replied, 'The Oval Cricket Ground.' And then, in a sentence which worried me deeply, he declared, 'It will be marvellous. The sun will shine and the grass will grow.' But what about the rain, the clover, the weeds, the harrowing, the rolling, the grazing? Ever since that day I have had grave doubts as to whether a man with so little understanding of grass should be allowed to govern.

Other worrying thoughts raced through my head as I ambled through the Dorset meadows on a so-called break. The blades of grass, shimmering as they yielded to the sea breezes, licked the top of my boots; here at home they hardly touch the laces. I thought about my flock of Dorset sheep and felt I should grab a pocketful of their native grass and take it home for them, like seaside rock to a child. On the other hand, Dorset seems to have a large number of Suffolk sheep, and perhaps I ought to grab a few handfuls of our grass and post it to them. I am sure that even sheep appreciate home cooking.

But I am not motivated by sheer envy when I spy my neighbour's flourishing grass. The point is that not until the grass is growing vigorously will it be time to turn out the stock that have been wintering in the farm-yard. For them it will be a blessed release, for no matter how comfortable you try to make a yard, farm animals naturally belong in wide open spaces. And, more to the point, this farmer gets fed up with the daily routine of carting feed. It has been going on now since the end of October and I am at the point where the sight of another mangel-wurzel will make me sick. I planted them, hoed them, lifted them, carted them, and now six months later I am still picking them up one by one, dropping them in a bucket and placing them before cattle. I am at the point where I can almost recognise individual ones and if it goes on much longer I shall be giving them names. Even worse, next week I shall be sowing next winter's crop. Torture by mangel-wurzels.

But even when the carting stops and the yard gates are opened wide on to the meadows, will the stock be any happier? If the sheep are anything to judge by, not necessarily. After three months of hustling and barging at the trough, dragging wiry hay from the rack with their teeth and living closer to their fellow sheep than naturally inclined, they still think that something is greener beyond the fence.

A couple of weeks ago, I turned them out on to a pasture bristling with grasses of countless variety and specially planted herbs. But they hardly bent their heads to taste it. They stood at the gate bleating to come home. If they could take one luxury with them to the desert meadow, they explained, it would be a farm-yard and a man with a bucket. I shall decline the invitation.

I T NEVER PAYS to go to plough with a heavy heart. The furrow is too narrow to accommodate human regret and remorse; it has its work cut out to find even room for the large feet of the cart-horses. They have their moods too, when ploughing, but it only ever seems to be willingness or idleness. I can never detect in the horse's attitude that he has much going through his mind other than thoughts of getting back to his manger.

That is not to underestimate his intelligence, for a good plough-horse is a clever beast. He knows precisely where to walk, when to turn, where to pull, while sensing the mood of the man steering the plough. Well, I must admit that my cart-horses have had some pretty glum moods wafting in their direction this ploughing season, and if I have appeared in any way ungrateful for their gargantuan efforts, I apologise.

The ploughing has been grim this year. We have been deluged with rain on a scale I have not witnessed in my short farming career. Arid ditches have become raging torrents, rainwater hangs in puddles in the hoof-prints left by the horses, the sheep are turning meadows into quagmires.

After the long drought the rain is welcome. But its effect on the ploughing has been disastrous, for the soil is so wet that it has ceased to behave like proper soil should, and has taken on the texture of an over-moist Christmas pudding. Consequently, in the same way that a gooey pud sticks to the spoon the earth is clinging to the plough as if its life depended on it; and even if it relinquishes its clinch on the breast it will not fall away as a well-behaved slice of soil should. Instead of collapsing neatly against the previous furrow it stands stubbornly upright, heavy, moist and immovable, so that the full weight of a boot against it is necessary to get the cursed earth to lie down.

What makes this depressing for the ploughman is the thought that for all his efforts to get horses and plough repeatedly along the field (I walk eleven miles to plough one acre), he might be wasting his time. For the purpose of ploughing is to tuck away last season's soil and bring to the surface fresh earth in which to plant the seeds. This trick only works if the ploughman turns the land completely; if he merely stands it on end as I seem to be doing, last year's crop will grow again along with a flourish of weeds. Disaster for the organic farmer who has no chemical remedy to check unwanted regrowth.

But I am doing my best, and so are the horses in what is turning out to be a strenuous phase of the year. But there are areas in which I have not done my best, and I am now paying the price. The field I am currently ploughing grew wheat and oats last year. The wheat was successfully cut with our binder, a lightweight device compared with a modern piece of farm machinery. But I was not so lucky with the oats. A rain-storm in July flattened them making cutting with a binder a near-impossibility. So my neighbour brought his combine-harvester, then his tractor and heavy trailer to take the grain, then a bigger tractor and baler to gather the straw, and finally another trailer to cart the bales. I pay the price every time my plough hits that patch of land, for where the unpressured wheat grew we fling the soil aside with the ease of a child playing in a sandpit; but as soon as we meet the strip where the oats grew the horses groan, the leather collars creek and my hands can hardly keep the plough on course through the compacted earth.

Old and new technology cannot be mixed. A heavy tractor sprinted along one of our farm tracks recently and left ruts so deep that as soon as they freeze, they will be sure to make a horse stumble. He was doing a job which the horse could easily have done had I found time and made the effort. Now the track is a sorry sight and will stay that way till the spring. By contrast, the field from which we carted mangel-wurzels for three days solid, using horse and cart to remove an estimated twenty tonnes, shows no marks of anything having been across it.

Every time I trudge the furrow, I bitterly regret allowing tractors on the land. Their speed and power does not compensate for the scars they leave on this little farm. Every furrow makes me want to pledge never to have one here again. But I doubt I have the strength to resist it. We are not all jolly fellows following the plough. I am sorry if I have spoilt your biscuit-tin lids for you.

'ONLY FOUR FURROWS to go,' I muttered as I strode across the frozen clods of earth. I paced it out again and, sure enough, four more miserable rounds with the plough and the winter's ploughing would be done. Not that I should grumble. Derek, the old horseman, had gamely volunteered to finish the headland, which is generally reckoned to be the most gruelling of all the ploughing tasks. This is the strip around the edge, about five yards wide, which is left when you have ploughed up and down the field. You go round and round the headland until either you drop, or the horses do, or the job is done. At one stage I really thought it might be the horses which would not finish the course, for after a mere couple of hours when normally they would hardly have raised a heavy breath let alone a sweat, old Star and Blue were dripping like heavyweights after a title fight. Tough old Derek, needless to say, was untouched by the effort.

But although ploughing stiff and cloddy headlands is a fight every inch of the way (remember, this is the land on which the horses have trodden repeatedly when turning at the ends of the furrows) there is a deep satisfaction in providing the frame, as it were, to an artful piece of ploughing. Although to tell the truth this year's ploughing has been indifferent, not the work of an Old Master.

I paced the frozen ground again just to reassure myself that there were really only four and not five gruesome furrows to go, and as I turned to walk back to the farm-yard I noticed a wall of chilly fog edging towards me. The frost had not lifted all day and it was bitterly cold, but as the fog overtook me some great refrigerator door opened and the temperature dived. I groped my way back to the farm-yard to continue work on yet another artistic effort.

This one is unashamedly born of the romantic school; devised to pluck heart-strings that twang whenever they see Constable's 'Hay Wain'. It is my lambing yard, built amid the soft red brick of the farm-yard wall, sheltered on two sides by the embrace of the black wooden barn, bedded with golden straw and roofed with thatch of our own growing. The sheep are mere extras.

But the centrepiece is the shepherd's hut which has stood idle by the house all summer waiting for its days of glory. We trundled it into position last week and it slotted into our scene like the final piece in a child's farm-yard jigsaw. Our blacksmith had fabricated a chimney to match a tiny stove which I had found; I had dusted off the hurricane lamps, chopped logs small enough to feed the stove, and gathered all the potions and appliances that are part of lambing, even down to the half-bottle of whisky to steady the shepherd's hand.

For light reading I stowed away a copy of *Walk Soft in the Fold* by David B. Nixon. This is a treasure and a comfort, for not only is it a tale well told of a young lad apprenticed to a shepherd of the old school, but scattered throughout the text are nuggets of wisdom which no modern text on sheep husbandry would impart.

For example, '. . . he took a clean piece of straw and gently pushed it up the lamb's nose – the lamb gave a great sneeze. "That be better," said the old man.' Since reading that, I have stirred life into several new-born lambs with no more than a wisp of straw. I have yet to try the trick of feeding ivy to a ewe that is off her food, but no doubt I shall. As the frost settled heavy for the night, the first lamb was born. Lambing had officially started, and I set a match to the kindling in the stove.

I went back to the house for a bottle of milk, tea and warm clothes for the night, anticipating that this year's lambing, set in my idyllic frame, would be one to remember. But as I made my way back to the hut I glanced at the ewe and sensed something was wrong. A second lamb was being born and was firmly stuck. I went to the hut for my lambing bag and found a thick, black smog oozing through every crack in the door. I flung open the door and a wall of smoke fell on me. It was like being inside a kipper-curing shed. The stove, untested till now, was old and leaking. I struggled to haul the lamb from the ewe and it was dead. Half an hour later she gave birth to a third, dead also. No matter how carefully the romantic farmer tries to paint the perfect picture, Nature always smudges it.

D O NOT BOTHER to ask how we are. Never in the brief history of this farm have so many of us been on the sick-list. Nothing too serious, you understand, but several of us are sufficiently lame and cronky to have brought to a halt the vital cultivations that spring demands. We still have acres of land to plough before the spuds can go in; there are meadows pleading for the chain-harrows to drag from them the dead tufty grass of last winter. But looking at me and the cart-horses, I must be realistic and admit that the next seven days are hardly likely to find any of us in harness again. Lest you should expend all your sympathy on the sick horses, I will trouble you with my symptoms first.

Last week I ploughed long and hard with a plough I had not

used before. Breaking in a new plough is as gruelling as mastering a new pair of stiff leather boots: nothing feels right for the first day and every step needs to be forethought if accidents are to be avoided. But I was not careful enough. By the end of a day in which I had fought the plough every inch of the way down the furrow, I had a dose of tennis-elbow which would do credit to an entire Wimbledon fortnight. I am left with a piercing ache which swells at the merest sight of a heavy bucket of pig swill. It is not sufficient to stop me working, just enough to cloud every day with a tetchy temper.

As for Star, the senior cart-horse, I am not certain what happened to him but at the same time that I was wrenching my elbow he was bruising his neck. I noticed he was not walking as straight and true in the furrow as his sixteen years have taught him and put it down to bloody-mindedness. But when it got to the point where he was contorting his body to such an extent that he was leaning forty-five degrees from the vertical, I decided it was time for home. Removing his collar revealed a lump. The vet examined it and we came to the conclusion that some equine skirmish had taken place in the yard (tempers do fray in late winter) and that old Star had been the loser. It was either a bite, or a kick, or a nudging into a gate-post; but for Star it was the end of his working week till the swelling went down.

Which brings us to Prince, the baby in the stable. A couple of days ago I harnessed him to the chain-harrows and headed for the meadows. We had three glorious hours combing the sward, ripping out the dead grass so the young shoots could breathe and grow. The vivid scent of freshly harrowed grass was intoxicating and on his return to the stable Prince would surely have licked his lips had they not been so sore. His tender young mouth, rested through the long winter months, had not taken kindly to the bit. I was advised that zinc and castor oil, as used on babies' bottoms, will have an equally soothing effect on Prince's mouth. As soon as I can find a baby buggy big enough for him to sit in, we shall be heading for Mothercare.

But by chance a leaflet arrived this week which may solve all our problems. It is offering cures for all ills by merely taking extracts from various wild flowers. The brochure boasts, '. . . simple and natural way of establishing complete equilibrium and harmony . . . by means of wild flowers'. If anywhere needs a little harmony and equilibrium at the moment, it is this farmer and his horses. There are thirty-eight different remedies on offer and looking through the symptoms they are designed to alleviate, I fear we might be in need of all of them.

Gorse, for example, is for pessimism and defeatism: we will take a gallon of that. Cherry Plum, on the other hand, is for 'uncontrolled, irrational thoughts': I think we may make a cocktail of that with a stiff measure of Chestnut ('for refusing to learn by experience') and a hefty swig of Vervain ('for having fanatical beliefs'). Do not think I am mocking Dr Bach's famous tried and tested remedies; I have a mind wide open to homeopathy. It is just a question of deciding which cure to go for. Perhaps extract of Holly will be the one. It is 'for hatred, envy and suspicion'. You see, Star hates the horse that bit him, envies the others for being free of pain and suspects Blue is to blame for it all. Prince, with the sore lips, hates me for making his mouth uncomfortable, envies the horses left in the stable while he has to work and suspects me of deliberately making his life miserable. I, on the other hand, hate them all for going sick at a time when the work is pressing, envy all other farmers who are getting on with the job and am deeply suspicious that it is some plot nature has hatched against me. Yes, I think a stiff dose of Holly. As if we weren't sufficiently prickly customers already.

H AS MEDICINE YET recognised a distinct disorder called Post-potato-planting Syndrome? My symptoms are manic depressive, swinging from the height of euphoria when it takes all my self-control to prevent me from parading around the village singing and rejoicing, 'They're in, they're done. They're planted for another year.' To brooding despair when I catch sight of the potato field at a wrong angle. One glance will set my self-respect into a deep nose-dive.

I blame my suffering on a spiritual experience some years ago on the Yorkshire Wolds. I was driving westwards towards the setting sun and ahead of me was a field into which had recently been planted potatoes. The land was oddly shaped and undulated, so the ridges left by the potato-planting machine made dazzling curves and patterns as the shadows moved across them. The trees and hedges were in bud and as I stopped to watch this piece of living art, the beauty that can dwell in a properly laid-out potato field lodged for ever in my soul.

Every year I have tried to re-create it here, but with horses it is very difficult. It only takes one side-step by one animal and if you do not have a firm grip of your ridger, it will dive to the side and the symmetry is gone. That one ripple amid the linear ridges can be seen a mile off. The spuds are none the worse for it, of course, but old horsemen had their pride and would have had to suffer the mocking of their fellows if their work was not entirely on the straight and narrow. I have to suffer the occasional critic.

But this year it went better than ever before. I took the fifty-year-old potato ridger to the blacksmith and had new threads welded so that I could make adjustments which had previously been impossible. I worked the land and carefully drew the furrows into which we dropped the seed potato. Dilly came to help. 'Have you ever shown potatoes at the village show?' I asked him. 'I did one year,' he announced to the entire field, 'but I had to withdraw. Tater was so big I couldn't ger it down side o' the house!'

The seed planted in the furrows, I gathered myself together for the final artistic touch. Horses and ridger must now be driven precisely between the furrows so that the soil which is thrown to either side covers the seeds and leaves a perfect ridge of soil above the fledgeling spud. To my surprise, we did not make a half bad job of it. You must understand that 'half bad' is as near to perfection as anybody gets round here. Had Michelangelo turned to a Suffolk farmer to ask his opinion of the Sistine Chapel, he would have been told it wasn't 'a half bad job at all!'

So I was happy the potatoes were planted, pleased it went well and overjoyed that the tedious task was over; yet niggled by the wiggles that made it a less than perfect job. Depressed by that thought, my mind became further saddened by the thought that the end of one job only means the start of the next. I had foolishly thought that once the spuds were in I could take a breath, have a few days off. But sheep need to be moved and fencing with them; the oats are ready for horse-hoeing and the wheat and barley will soon be ready too. I was trying to crystallise in my mind what my predicament reminded me of, when a letter arrived.

I have had many helpful suggestions concerning the painting of my Ransome's Threshing Drum which I wish to decorate in its original pink paint; a distinctive and virulent shade. A Mrs Burwell of Downham Market remembers her father mixing his own and falling so in love with it that he painted the outside privy with what came to be known in their family as 'drum pink'. She tells me the pink paint still haunts her, for she lately saw the very same shade on the walls of a tea-room of a National Trust property in Norfolk. I may be giving them a call.

But Mr Williams's letter was the one that brought me up short, for it arrived just as I was in the depths of my post-potato-planting gloom. He tells me that some years ago he lived in South Queensferry at the end of the Forth Railway Bridge and 'acquired a sample of what the painters used on their unending job'. He still has it in his garage and may send me a drum of it . . .

Grateful though I am, I cannot say I am looking forward to it. With the busiest time of the farming year fast approaching, with hay-making and thistle-bashing just around the corner, I hardly need a reminder that painting the Forth Bridge and running this farm are occupations too close for comfort. Perhaps it is time for a lengthy cup of tea and a wallow in a pink National Trust tea-room – in the interests of research, of course.

Second Crop

I T HAS BEEN one of those weeks when we seem to have been nervously looking over our shoulders, glancing to the skies and wondering where the fickle finger of fate is going to strike next. I fear it will be here. My unease results from a report which said that the chances of the average person being struck by lightning have diminished greatly over the last fifty years. This is because far fewer people work on the land, so not as many poor souls are in a position to be struck these days. It makes sense. Farmers these days ride around in tractors on vast, insulating rubber tyres and my school-boy memories of the behaviour of static electricity seem to suggest that if you are cocooned in a shell, as in a tractor cab, you are safe anyway.

But none of this is any comfort to me. Most of my working days are spent grasping aged cast-iron farm implements connected by steel chains to horses whose only contact with the ground is through thick, highly conductive horseshoes. Only the Empire State Building seems a more probable candidate for a lightning strike than me. And since the weather forecasts have been full of nothing but hints of 'thundery lows' coming up from France, you can imagine my unease. At the top of our farm stand the charred remains of three great oaks; all vestiges of life have been burnt from them but they still stand as a gaunt reminder of the force of a bolt from the blue. That could be me up there, welded to my plough handle. Think of that.

For comfort I consulted the vintage farming tomes and in particular a pocket-book published in 1911 called *Weather Wisdom in Agriculture*. It tells me that 'the meteorological office is prepared to despatch a telegraphic warning of the likelihood of any such disturbances'. Fair enough, but by the time Mr McCaskill has tapped out a warning on his Morse key and the post office at this end has called in a boy scout to decode it, we would all be as crisp as a slice of overdone bacon. It is said that animals can be harbingers of thunder, but I fear on this farm the message may become confused. For instance, cows are said to be reliable indicators of stormy weather ahead:

When a cow tries to scratch its ear,
It means a shower is very near.
When it clumps its side with its tail,
Look out for thunder, lightning and hail.

Not on this farm. That rather brassy cow of ours, Sage, swipes her tail on her flank in the same way that some old vamp will swing her handbag when the fleet's in. This is a signal to the rest of the cows to follow her over to the other side of the field in the hope that some hunky young bull might have appeared. As weather forecasts go, she is about as useful as a length of dead seaweed.

Trying to put all these worries behind me, I decided to throw myself into my work, and set to harrow the potato baulks. The baulks are the long ridges beneath which the seed potatoes lie and from which will shortly sprout the green shoots of this year's crop. But until they do the weeds are having a field day and if I did not drag them out with the spiky, curved baulk-harrow, they would become established. Never having done this before, I decided to use our steadiest horse, Blue. I often say of Blue that he is the sort of horse to whom I could say, 'Stand still', go home for lunch and still find him in the same spot, thinking very slowly, when I returned. If they ever need a Suffolk Punch to work the slopes of Mount Etna this is the animal: it could erupt and he would not flinch.

But this day, with the thunder rumbling around, things were different. We harrowed the entire field and had only one baulk left to do. I dropped the cord to adjust the harrows and for no reason that I can think of, Blue took a step forward of his own accord. I did not reach for the line to his bit; having shouted, 'Whooah', I never believed he would move another inch. But he did. He was terrified. He charged forward, accelerated to a gallop and headed for home; luckily he broke the iron chain that connected him to the harrows otherwise they and the stable door would have eventually met and there could have been a very nasty accident.

I have since thought long and hard about what sent this most stable of horses into shock. I suspect Alice's growing, and admittedly rather odd-looking, black and white piglets. They were fenced into a field adjacent to the spuds, and Blue may not have spotted them as they rooted between the thick clumps of clover. Perhaps one piglet glanced up, Blue caught sight of it in the corner of his eye and panicked. Anyway, the horse is safe and unharmed. I even take some consolation from the fact that having had one bolt from the Blue this season, I will not be struck again in the same place.

9
Hallelujah!
The Year is Done

B Y THE TIME you read this, I gravely suspect that our young sow Phoebe will have caused us dreadful embarrassment. If you think your relations are awkward at Christmas, count yourself lucky.

Having reared her last litter of piglets to the ripe old age of ten weeks, Phoebe is now ready to turn her back on them and give her undivided attention to the founding of the next litter. At least, *I* am ready for her to do so. If she is not of the same mind there is little she can do about it, for I have loaded her into the trailer, hauled her round the pigsty and settled her on straw where the next love of her life awaits.

If this seems brusque, it is a far cry from the modern way of rearing litters which removes suckling pigs from the teat at the tender age of three weeks. We leave ours to suck their mother till they are happy and plump, and of a size to knock her around if she fails to keep them under control. Far from weeping at the loss of her offspring I have never seen a pig go up the ramp of a trailer as fast as our Phoebe when she spotted an opportunity for a quick escape from a family Christmas. And if the remarriage seems to be a little swift after the family break-up, this is merely because pigs come into season two or three days after weaning and the opportunity must be seized. The boar will see to that.

I cannot think of any attractive way to describe the visiting Large Black boar. Even though there is little malice in him, there seems to be more than enough lurking menace to persuade me to move swiftly at feeding time. He is hefty, thick-set and very – er – masculine. He froths at the mouth. But Phoebe adores him, and no part of her black bulk does she allow to go unsniffed by her slimy-snouted suitor. Nor does she take it, so to speak, lying down. She cavorts around the sty, kicking straw aside, squealing and giggling like a schoolgirl confronting her pop idol. And it is these squeals of porcine delight which I fear may lead to trouble; for this year we have decided to hold a farm-yard nativity play. And what am

I going to say to the audience if, half-way through 'Silent Night', Phoebe gets a fit of the shrieking amorous giggles?

For the last couple of Christmases, I have never been able to sing a carol without realising what an ideal setting we could provide for a nativity play. Our lambing sheds are built of grown timbers and thatched with warm straw; our cattle eat their feed from real mangers and when the frosts come we are only too familiar with earth as hard as iron, water like a stone. We even have the cast. Our eight-year-old daughter wishes to play Mary but her ten-year-old brother will not be seen dead showing her any affection, and so refuses to play Joseph. He has decided to be the inn-keeper so that he can spend the entire play being miserable and grumpy. He will doubtless take after his father and become a farmer.

Although I have been offered a donkey, it seems only proper that our Suffolk Punches should haul the blessed couple to the stable. Our farm-worker friend Derek is going to wrap himself in old sacking and lead the horse through the yard. We shall gather a flock of young shepherds and they can abide with the long-suffering Dorset sheep around the shepherd's hut which we will place near the gate. The ewes are due to start lambing on New Year's Day and I now regret not having sent the ram to work a couple of weeks sooner so that a couple of early lambs might have completed the scene. I think our sheep-dog, Flash, will have to abide in his kennel for although excellent with a flock, his relationship with others is strained and I foresee a situation where the infant Jesus (borrowed doll) will be hauled from the manger and dragged like a juicy bone into the corner. I did consider an impressionistic attempt to have our gloriously white cow, Sage, play the Angel Gabriel but her calf would surely try to follow. We are trying to create an atmosphere of dreamless sleep with silent stars going by, not a rodeo.

As I write, the performance is tomorrow and I am keeping my fingers crossed that a noisy upsurge of passion in our Phoebe is not going to coincide with the dignified and hushed coming down of the Angel of the Lord, played by the only boy in the village who can get a tune out of a trumpet. The only solution that crosses my mind if she does bellow is to drown her out with help from the bullocks. Lowing cattle are, after all, acceptable. In the end, if the worst should happen, I shall have to turn my back on the holy scene, replace my farmer's hat, and think of the lucrative litter to come. Glad tidings of great joy: for once, a profit cometh in the land.

As I WRITE, I am removing my trousers smeared with filth, disposing of the sweater that reeks of wet sheep and discarding my cap which, as I was bending to unblock a drain, fell into a vast lake of horse piddle.

Stinking farmer's clothes are not suitable garments in which to write a theatrical review, so for the next few hundred words imagine me in a fragrant white silk scarf and evening suit like Mr Levin in his prime, possibly carrying a cane with a silver handle. It is quite a feat of the imagination, but necessary if I am to give you a flavour of the last major theatrical event of 1992: our farm-yard nativity play.

Luck, broadly speaking, was on our side. The soprano did not fall off the straw-stack as, without as much as a wobble (creditable since she was thirty feet in the air and the stack is a bit on the rickety side), she sang all the verses of 'In the Bleak Midwinter'. This occupied those precious few moments between the setting of the sun (after which we dared not let the unaccustomed audience stumble from their seats on bales of straw) and the falling of total darkness (before which we dared not start the action). She did not even allow herself a giggle as the heifer chimed in with an ear-splitting *mooo* on the higher notes. The audience were not only transfixed by this celestial vision of a beautiful girl singing from the darkening clouds, but were also hemmed-in on all sides by cart-horses, cattle and sheep. Heaven above and hell all around them.

The narrator climbed on to a farm waggon and the story unfolded. The innkeeper (ten years old) gave much passion to his part, inspired by sheer delight at being able to tell his younger sister (the Virgin Mary) there was no room for her at his inn, no way. The massive brown frame of one of our Suffolk Punches lumbered from the darkness and stole the scene as he hauled Mary and Joseph to their stable. The shepherds piped, and were sore amazed (as well they might be) by the apparition of our teenage Gabriel on the stack with a trumpet, apparently playing a cross between the Coronation Fanfare and the Last Post.

But while we all sang 'The First Nowell', an unseen hitch occurred. Derek the horseman, who has probably never taken part in a theatrical event in his life, was supposed to take the horse and cart round the back, unhitch him and bring him in again bedecked with gold and gifts as the Three Kings' camel.

It is fortunate that Derek is a man of even temper, for at this point he and his camel could easily have got the hump. The only way round the farm buildings was blocked by a latecomer's car; he had to haul the reluctant cart-horse at top speed down the lane so he could cut across the field and still make it in time for the Three Kings' entrance. My wife spotted his dilemma and signalled the accordion player to do more verses. The narrator intoned, '. . . and far away, in the East, three wise men . . .', as the lumbering horse was forced into a near-gallop down the lane and the heavy clatter of steel shoes on roadway split the air.

Gabriel socked us another unusual fanfare, and by the time we had all got through 'We Three Kings' with the baby in the real manger, the cow mooing, the sheep bleating and the Suffolk Punch standing magnificently to attention, it is fair to say there was not a dry eye in the house.

'The true spirit of Christmas,' wept one lady as she stumbled through the straw in the darkness. 'Moving, very very moving,' muttered another. An elderly but vital lady of ninety-three announced she was the great-grandmother of Jenny who had sung on the straw-stack, and that four generations of her family had been there to see it.

It was profitable: we raised £250 (all for the British Red Cross) and I seem to have done all right too. In order to spare our visitors a slow drowning in mud, a couple of local farmers donated straw to spread all over the yard. It is still there and is ready for the sheep, who will shortly be coming in to lamb. Without a hundred pairs of feet to kick it around, it would have been a sweaty job to spread it.

The Scrooge in me returning, I am planning another such event. Perhaps at Easter, we shall do the Stations of the Cross. I shall ask the audience each to carry a stake and process around the farm. Every time the script demands it, they will hammer it religiously into the ground. If it should so happen that they follow the line of the new fence I am planning, so much the better.